With le
Gra

520 D
Dempsey, Michael W.
Majesty of the heavens
LAMAN LIBRARY   ocm01047996

D1541178

520
D
Dempsey, Michael
The majesty of the heavens.

WM. F. LAMAN PUBLIC LIBRARY
CIVIC CENTER
NORTH LITTLE ROCK, ARKANSAS

145423

WM. F. LAMAN PUBLIC LIBRARY
CIVIC CENTER
NORTH LITTLE ROCK, ARKANSAS

145423

The Majesty of the Heavens

MICHAEL DEMPSEY, B.A.   JOAN PICK, B.Sc.

FOUNDATIONS OF SCIENCE LIBRARY

GREYSTONE PRESS/NEW YORK

WM. F. LAMAN PUBLIC LIBRARY
CIVIC CENTER
NORTH LITTLE ROCK, ARKANSAS

CHIEF EDITORS

Leslie Basford, B.Sc.   Philip Kogan, M.Sc.

ASSISTANT EDITORS

Michael Dempsey, B.A., Michael Gabb, B.Sc., Clare Dover, B.Sc.
Cyril Parsons, B.Sc., Joan Pick, B.Sc., Michael Chinery, B.A.
David Larkin, B.Sc., Paul Drury Byrne, B.Sc.

CONSULTANT EDITORIAL BOARD

Sir Lawrence Bragg, M.C., O.B.E., F.R.S., M.A., Nobel Laureate
Sir James Chadwick, F.R.S., Ph.D., M.Sc., Nobel Laureate
Norman Fisher, M.A.
Sir Harry Melville, K.C.B., F.R.S., Ph.D., D.Sc.
Professor J. Z. Young, F.R.S., M.A.

This new presentation assembles freshly edited material from
'Understanding Science' on one subject into a single volume.

Copyright © MCMLXV, MCMLXVI Sampson Low, Marston & Co. Ltd.

Library of Congress Catalog Card Number: 66-14640

Manufactured in U.S.A.

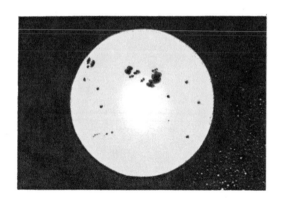

CONTENTS

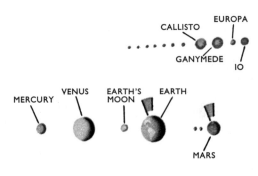

CALLISTO EUROPA

GANYMEDE IO

MERCURY VENUS EARTH'S MOON EARTH

MARS

JUPITER

CHAPTER ONE

The Solar System

THE SOLAR SYSTEM in which we live is a group of heavenly bodies consisting of one star (the Sun), nine major planets (including the Earth) and their satellites or moons, thousands of tiny planetoids or asteroids, comets and meteors. Only the Sun has any light of its own. The planets and their moons shine merely because they reflect the solar rays. The radius of the solar system, the distance from the Sun to the outermost known planet circling it, is over 3,500 million miles. It is very unlikely that ours is the only solar system in the whole universe; there are most probably millions of other stars possessing a system of circling planets.

Mercury is the smallest of the nine major planets of the solar system, with a diameter of only 3,100 miles (less than half that of the Earth). It is also the planet nearest the Sun, though the actual distance varies from 28,500,000 miles to 43,500,000

miles, for Mercury has a very eccentric, or elongated, orbit.

Many millions of years ago the strong gravitational pull of the Sun slowed down the spin of this small planet in such a way that now Mercury always presents the same face to the Sun. In other words the time it takes to revolve once on its axis is exactly the same as the time it takes to orbit the Sun (88 Earth days).

The difficulties of examining Mercury from the Earth are considerable. Firstly, it is a very small planet which never comes closer to the Earth than 50,000,000 miles, and secondly, it is only visible for a short time after sunset and just before sunrise. It can, however, be viewed during the day through telescopes which are shielded from the Sun. It then appears dull white in colour with yellowish tinges.

The planet Venus which circles the Sun between Mercury and Earth is

4

SATURN

TITAN

NEREID

NEPTUNE

PLUTO

URANUS

hard to miss rather than hard to see. Few people can have failed to notice the brilliant white 'star' that becomes visible soon after sunset, and long before any other star is visible. After sunset Venus is known as the Evening Star, and before sunrise, the Morning Star.

Venus is much the same size as the Earth (diameter 7,700 miles) and has a nearly circular orbit like our own. Its average distance from the Sun is just 67,200,000 miles and it never varies more than one million miles from this figure. Venus comes closer to the Earth than any other planet, but even then is 26,000,000 miles away. Occasionally it is seen to pass across the Sun, and this is known as the transit of Venus. Since its orbit is on a different plane from that of the Earth, these transits are extremely rare (the next is due in the year AD 2004).

It is not possible to see the surface of Venus because it is always covered in dense clouds. And owing to this, it is impossible to determine how long it takes for the planet to turn on its axis. Many astronomers believe that a Venusian day lasts for about 30 of our

days, but it is difficult to tell when there are no surface markings to go by.

Venus' atmosphere consists mainly of carbon dioxide, and the temperature of the clouds ranges from about 55° C. on the side facing the Sun to below freezing point on the other side. It is doubtful that the clouds themselves are made up of water vapour like our own.

Probably the surface temperatures of the planet are much higher than those of the clouds, for the layer of carbon dioxide would act as a great blanket, trapping the Sun's heat like a greenhouse does. Some astronomers picture the surface to be one great wind-eroded monotonous desert.

For many years the Earth was treated as a very special planet, in fact as the centre of the whole universe. But really the status of our world is simply that of one of the smaller planets in the solar system.

The Earth is the third planet in line from the Sun, around which it orbits at an average distance of 93,000,000 miles. Spinning on its tilted axis, it takes about 24 hours to complete one revolution (a day) and about 365 days to complete one orbit of the Sun (a year). The Earth's diameter is 7,926 miles across the equator but 27 miles less across the poles, owing to its slightly flattened shape. The atmosphere is composed mainly of nitrogen and oxygen, and shields us from much of the Sun's fierce heat. Temperatures at the surface vary considerably. The lowest so far recorded was $-84.5°$ C. $(-120°$ F.) near the South Pole, and

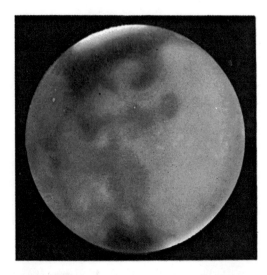

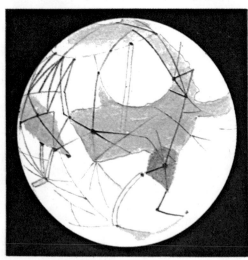

(*Above*) **Mars as it appears through a powerful telescope.** (*Below*) **A sketch of the Martian 'canals'.**

the highest, $57.8°$ C. $(136°$ F.), in Libya, North Africa. Over two-thirds of the Earth's surface is covered with water.

Our planet has one satellite, the Moon, which circles it in just over 27 days. Our Moon is described more fully in chapter 4.

The Earth has one very important claim to distinction as the home of Man. It is the only planet in our solar system where conditions are exactly right for life as we know it to exist. This, however, is not surprising, for life forms have evolved which suit their surroundings. It is also one of the most beautiful planets. Seen from the Moon it would appear as a large, greenish-blue disc with shimmering blue oceans and sparkling white polar ice caps, and with the continents clearly superimposed upon it.

Mars, the first planet beyond the orbit of the Earth, is the one which has attracted the most attention and caused the most speculation through the ages. It is just over one-tenth the size of our planet and turns on its axis once every 24½ hours. Mars takes 687 Earth days to circle the Sun but has a very elliptical orbit. At one point it is only 128,000,000 miles from the Sun, and at another about 155,000,000 miles. The axis upon which Mars spins is tilted at an angle to the plane of its orbit, which means that this planet has seasons just as we do, though they are about twice as long as ours. Mars has two small moons, Deimos and Phobos.

Mars is often thought of as the planet most likely to support life as we know it. Yet conditions there are very different from our own. The thin atmosphere has only a very small amount of oxygen, the remainder being made up mainly of nitrogen. Being farther away from the Sun than

Saturn with its rings.

canals. If they do exist, it is probable that they are natural features, but they may be an optical illusion.

The best evidence for life on Mars consists of large greenish areas which may represent some form of simple plant life.

Between Mars and the orbit of the next planet, Jupiter, is a wide gap occupied by a number of asteroids, tiny planets, mostly little more than great lumps of rock. The largest of these, Ceres, has a diameter of 480 miles. Something like 2,000 of these asteroids have been observed, though there may well be as many as 100,000 altogether. The origin of the asteroids can only be guessed at. Perhaps they resulted from the break-up of a planet which passed too close to Jupiter, or perhaps several planets formed in this region, then crashed together and shattered into pieces.

Jupiter is the giant of the solar system, measuring 86,800 miles across. Its average distance from the Sun is 483,300,000 miles and it takes nearly twelve of our years to complete its orbit.

the Earth, Mars is naturally colder. On the equator, day temperatures may rise to almost $27°$ C. ($80°$ F.), but nights are extremely cold. About two-thirds of the planet's surface consists of desert-like regions, ranging from deep red to bright orange in colour. They may be sand deserts or simply vast stretches of reddish rock. This is what gives Mars its characteristic reddish colour, even when viewed with the naked eye. The polar areas have very interesting snow caps which shrink to mere patches in the Martian summer but spread out half-way to the equator in the winter. They are probably not more than a few inches deep and may be simply a frosty covering.

The so-called 'canals' which lace the deserts have caused a great deal of speculation, and it has been suggested that they were built by former inhabitants to distribute water from the snow caps across a planet which was slowly 'drying up'. There is, however, no evidence to support this appealing idea, and some astronomers claim that they have never seen the

Jupiter, showing the Red Spot.

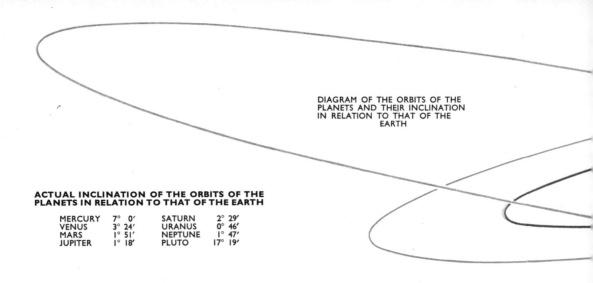

DIAGRAM OF THE ORBITS OF THE
PLANETS AND THEIR INCLINATION
IN RELATION TO THAT OF THE
EARTH

**ACTUAL INCLINATION OF THE ORBITS OF THE
PLANETS IN RELATION TO THAT OF THE EARTH**

MERCURY	7° 0'	SATURN	2° 29'
VENUS	3° 24'	URANUS	0° 46'
MARS	1° 51'	NEPTUNE	1° 47'
JUPITER	1° 18'	PLUTO	17° 19'

Jupiter has an unusual atmosphere which is divided into several broad belts, each of which moves at a different speed. The belts are constantly changing colour and shift their position slightly from year to year. But the number always remains the same. Apart from these markings there is also a Red Spot, a large pinkish-grey patch which cannot be part of the planet's surface because it moves at very irregular speeds. It has been suggested that it is some immense floating body.

The surface of Jupiter cannot be examined through a telescope because of the dense atmospheric clouds which hang above it. The atmosphere is believed to be made up mainly of hydrogen, methane and ammonia at an average temperature of around $-130°$ C. These two facts alone are enough to rule out the remotest possibility of any form of Earthly life being able to exist. But that is not all. The surface of the planet is covered with a layer of ice perhaps 17,000 miles thick. Jupiter has twelve moons which circle it in different orbits. Four of the moons are bright enough to be seen with a small telescope.

Saturn is probably the most beauti-ful object in the sky, chiefly on account of the broad rings which encircle it. But being so far away (mean distance from the Sun 886,200,000 miles) it appears as a dull yellowish 'star' to the naked eye. This planet is quite small compared to its gigantic neighbour Jupiter, but even so it has an equatorial diameter of over 75,000 miles. The diameter across the poles is 8,000 miles less, so that there is a considerable polar flattening. Despite the fact that this planet is some 750 times the size of our own, its force of gravity is little more than the Earth's, for the materials of which it is made are not packed so tightly. Like Jupiter, Saturn has a thick atmosphere of hydrogen, methane and ammonia below which lies a deep layer of ice.

The spectacular rings — there are three of them, one inside the other — measure over 170,000 miles from edge to edge, but they are only between 10 and 40 miles thick. Viewed edge on they appear as an extremely thin disc, cutting the planet along its equator. They are composed of millions and millions of small pieces of rock, probably encased in ice. The rings may have been produced by the break-up of a satellite, or perhaps they are

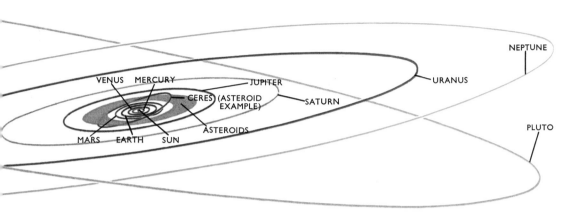

made up of matter 'left over' when the planet was formed. Saturn has nine moons circling around it. Most of them are smaller than the Earth's moon, but one, the giant Titan, has a diameter of 3,500 miles and is the only satellite known to possess its own atmosphere.

The next planet in line from the Sun, Uranus, was only discovered in 1781, but it can just be seen with the naked eye. Through a telescope it appears as a pale green disc without distinct surface markings. It is difficult to learn much about this planet owing to the fact that it is 1,783,000,000 miles from the Sun. One unusual feature of Uranus, however, is the fact that its axis is tilted from the vertical, not just $3°$ like Jupiter's, or even $23\frac{1}{2}°$ like the Earth's, but fully $98°$

Neptune, the last of the giant planets, was discovered in 1846 by the German astronomer Johann Galle. It was discovered as a result of apparent irregularities in the movements of Uranus which could only be explained by the presence of another planet. It has a diameter of about 28,000 miles and is, on the average, about 2,794,-000,000 miles from the Sun. As might be expected with an outer planet, it takes a long time to complete its orbit round the Sun, about 165 years.

Neptune is so distant from the Earth that it cannot be seen with the naked eye. Even through a telescope it appears only as a small green disc, with rather light bands around its equatorial and polar regions. Neptune has two moons circling it, Triton and Nereid.

Pluto is the outermost known planet, some 3,670,000,000 miles from the Sun. It is also the most recent of the major planetary bodies to be discovered. Pluto was predicted by the American astronomer, Lowell, in 1905, but it was not until 1930, fourteen years after Lowell's death, that it was actually discovered. Pluto has a diameter of about 3,600 miles and takes a little less than 250 years to circle the Sun. Beyond this, little is known, for the most powerful telescopes show this planet as little more than a yellowish spot.

Whether or not there are other planets in our solar system, waiting to be discovered, only time will tell. It has been suggested that Pluto is the nearest of a number of smaller bodies on the outer fringe of the solar system.

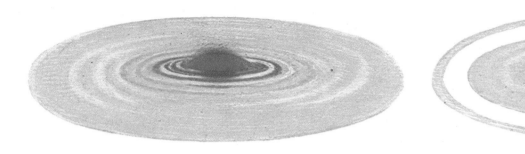

CHAPTER TWO

The Formation of the Planets

AT LEAST ONE aspect of the Earth's origin arouses little dispute. All of the evidence points to the fact that the solar system (including the Sun, the nine major planets and their satellites or moons, over 1,500 minor planets (planetoids or asteroids) and countless comets and meteors) is a complete unit, and that the whole family of planets has a common parentage. Two of the most important pieces of evidence in favour of this are the fact that the planets orbit the Sun in more or less the same plane, and that all orbit in the same direction. This *orderliness* tends to refute an alternative view that the Sun, by means of its immense gravitational attraction, 'acquired' the planets one by one through the ages.

Dissent begins when it comes to the actual parentage of the planets. Perhaps the Sun itself can be held responsible. The chemical composition of the Earth and the Sun is very similar. It is possible that all of the elements found on Earth are represented in the Sun; certainly most are. And their relative amounts are very similar too—with two great exceptions: hydrogen and helium make up approximately 99% of the Sun,

but both are extremely rare on Earth as gases. This, however, can be explained by the fact that hydrogen and helium are the lightest elements and the gravitational attraction of the young Earth was probably insufficient to retain its share of these free gases within the primeval atmosphere. But the chemical composition of the Earth (with the exceptions already noted) compares closely with that of other stars too. Thus, the possibility that the planets originated not from the Sun but from some other star cannot be ruled out.

In 1796 Pierre Simon Laplace, a French astronomer and mathematician, put forward the first of the nebular theories of the formation of the Earth. He supposed that at one time the whole solar system was a great nebulous cloud of gases, slowly rotating in space. The centre of the nebula was fairly dense compared with the outermost parts which, distended by heat, reached farther out from the Sun than the present position of Saturn. Laplace attempted to explain the formation of the planets (only seven were known in his day) by arguing that as the nebula cooled and contracted it would rotate faster

Laplace's hypothesis (now rejected) suggested that the planets were formed from gaseous rings shed one after another from a contracting and revolving cloud of gases.

and faster until centrifugal force near the rim exceeded the gravitational attraction of the mass. When this happened, a ring of gas would be shed from the edge (rather as nails would be flung from a revolving magnet at a certain speed). This would slowly gather into a gaseous sphere and condense into a planet circling round the central mass. As the nebula continued to shrink successive rings would be shed, each forming a planet. Laplace's theory, though popular for some time, was eventually found to be mathematically impossible.

In recent years the gaseous nebula hypothesis has been revived in a number of modified forms. In one of these it is suggested that early in its life the Sun was surrounded by a large nebula of gases and solid dust particles. As this nebula revolved with the Sun local concentrations of matter developed, and hence local fields of gravitation. More particles were drawn to the local concentrations until solid cores were formed,

It is quite probable that the young protoplanets, whatever their mode of origin, grew to their present size by sweeping up 'loose' material through their gravitational attraction as they circled the young Sun.

each surrounded by a gaseous envelope. One of these 'protoplanets' developed into the Earth.

It is suggested that at the same time the Sun was developing its present heat. As a result the gases surrounding the planets nearest it were strongly heated and began to escape into space (the molecules of gas became so agitated through heating that the planets' pull of gravity was not strong enough to hold them

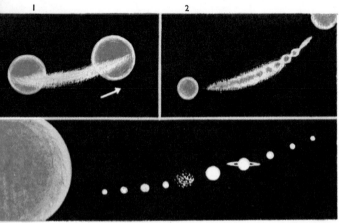

One theory of the formation of the planets. (1) A star grazed the Sun, pulling gases away from it and forming (2) a cigar-shaped cloud. (3) The cloud condenses into planets, the larger ones in the middle.

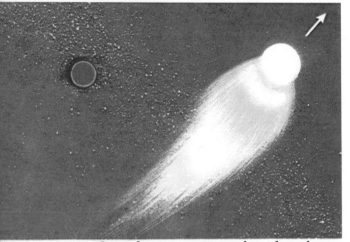

One theory suggests that the planets were formed from matter ejected from an exploding companion star of the Sun.

all). In this way the planet nearest to the Sun (Mercury) lost the whole of its atmosphere, while Venus and the Earth, the next two in line, were only able to hold a small percentage of theirs (almost all of the lightest gases, hydrogen and helium, escaped). Mars, although farther from the Sun than the Earth, was stripped almost entirely of its primeval atmosphere because it was so small (the smaller the planet the less its gravitational attraction). On the other hand, the giant planets farther away from the Sun (Jupiter and Saturn) retained the whole of their atmospheres.

There are a number of theories which can be grouped together as *catastrophic*. These suggest a sudden, catastrophic beginning to the solar system rather than the gradual evolutionary process so far described. Most are based upon a hypothetical encounter between the Sun and a passing star in the dim past. At the beginning of the present century, a popular theory was that the Sun almost collided with a passing star and was partly disrupted in the process. The passing of the star raised great gaseous tides on the Sun, and resulted in the ejection of a large stream of gas. This soon broke up into separate parts which by cooling, contraction and condensation developed into planets (the residue forming asteroids and comets). The planets would have been given their motion around the Sun by the gravitational attraction of the receding star. There are, however, a number of stumbling-blocks to this theory, one of the greatest being the problem of how the planets came to be pushed out to their present immense distances from the Sun.

This problem at least is solved by

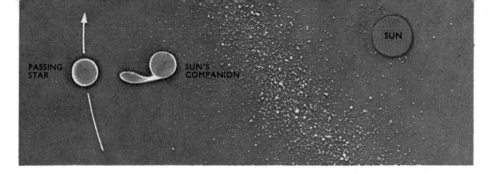

It has been suggested that the planets were formed from matter ejected from a companion star of the Sun due to the gravitational attraction of a passing star.

a recent theory in which the parent of the planets is taken to be not the Sun but another star. It has been suggested that the Sun might have been not a single star but a component of a binary system (two stars which orbit each other under the mutual attraction of their masses). If an 'outside' star approached close enough to the Sun's companion, then the 'tidal disruption' theory could account for the formation of the planets (the Sun's partner being disrupted rather than the Sun itself). If the disrupted star was already as far away from the Sun as, say, Jupiter is at present, the position of the planets would be easier to explain. The obvious problem here is to explain the disappearance of the other component of the binary system, and how the ejected material came under the Sun's control.

A promising variation of the binary concept suggests that the Sun's companion 'exploded' (stars have been known to do this when their supply of hydrogen has become exhausted), and that a small proportion of the ejected material was captured by the Sun and eventually formed the planets. This explains the disappearance of the parent star: it literally shot away into space from the recoil of the explosion.

These are just a few of the many theories and even more numerous problems connected with the origin of the Earth.

In the year 1650, Archbishop Ussher of Ireland concluded from studies of Biblical chronology that the Earth was created on 23 October 4004 B.C. (the time was later defined as 9.0 a.m.). This remained the official date of creation for the next hundred years or more. Yet in other religions the Earth is regarded as eternal in the respect that it always has been and always will be.

It was only at the turn of the nineteenth century that scientists entered what had previously been an exclusively theological field. This was when the new science of geology was being born. Geology is the study of the Earth's long past through the surface rocks and the fossils they contain (fossils had previously been dismissed as the work of the Devil). Layers of rock are like the pages of a history book to the geologist (though far more difficult to read, since many are torn and some missing) and it was soon found that they made up a 'book' which covered many millions of years of history.

In the nineteenth century, various attempts were made to estimate the age of the Earth. One involved an estimate of the time taken for the amount of salt in the waters of the oceans to accumulate to the present level. Another assumed (wrongly) that the Earth had gradually cooled from a molten state. As a result, in

13

the closing years of the last century, estimates of the Earth's age ranged from 20,000,000 to 100,000,000 years, and all were a long way out.

It was only the discovery of radio-activity in 1896 that paved the way to a more accurate estimate of the Earth's past. For radio-active elements, such as uranium, gradually break down or 'decay' into more stable elements (lead in this case) and the rate at which this happens can be calculated. So it is possible, by weighing the amount of lead produced at the expense of uranium in certain radio-active rocks, to determine the age of these rocks (a process known as uranium/lead dating). It is now known that some of the rocks in the Earth's crust are over 3,000,000,000 years old, and it is probable that the Earth itself is at least 4,000,000,000 years old.

It is interesting to note that some meteorites have been found to contain radio-active elements. This has made it possible to determine the age of the material and in most cases the answer is around 4,500,000,000 years old.

At some period during its very early life, the Earth most probably passed through a semi-molten phase. This was when the heaviest minerals sank towards the centre while the lightest rose to the surface and the remainder arranged themselves appropriately in between. Gradually the surface of the planet cooled and the minerals solidified to form a thin rock crust.

No one can say for sure how the continents came into being. They are like great 'plates' of granite 'floating' on the denser material beneath. Possibly, outpourings of the lightest materials gathered in great pools and upon cooling formed concentrations of granitic rock which laid the basis of the continental platforms. Many people believe that the continents crystallized in one or perhaps two great masses which broke up many millions of years later, the pieces drifting apart to the present positions of the land masses.

While the minerals of the Earth were arranging themselves, an immense amount of water vapour was being released from the heated interior into the primeval atmosphere where it formed a dense cloud over the whole planet. But no water appeared on the surface of the Earth, for raindrops were boiled back into vapour long before they could reach the intensely hot ground. When at last the crustal rocks had cooled sufficiently to allow rain to fall, a great deluge must have followed, out of which the young oceans were born. But the oceans have only reached their present extent by the addition of 'juvenile' water which has been constantly 'sweated' out from the Earth's interior throughout geological time.

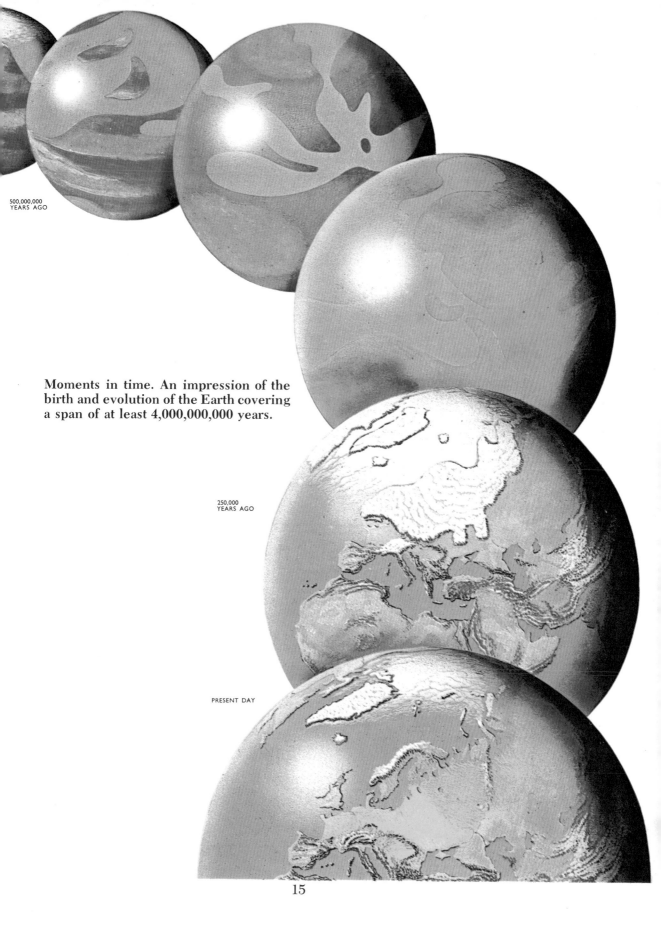

500,000,000
YEARS AGO

Moments in time. An impression of the
birth and evolution of the Earth covering
a span of at least 4,000,000,000 years.

250,000
YEARS AGO

PRESENT DAY

15

CHAPTER THREE

Precession

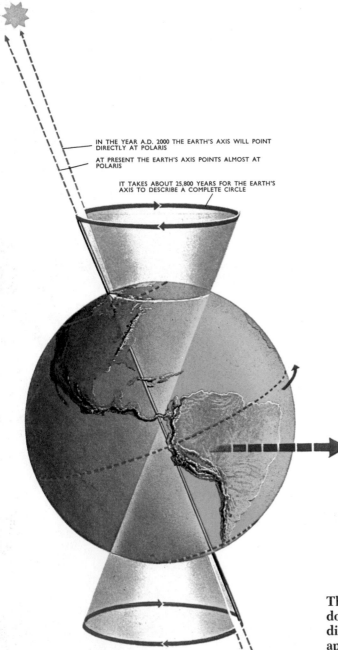

IN THE YEAR A.D. 2000 THE EARTH'S AXIS WILL POINT DIRECTLY AT POLARIS

AT PRESENT THE EARTH'S AXIS POINTS ALMOST AT POLARIS

IT TAKES ABOUT 25,800 YEARS FOR THE EARTH'S AXIS TO DESCRIBE A COMPLETE CIRCLE

THE EARTH rotates like a top upon its axis (a line drawn between the north and south poles), completing one revolution in about 24 hours. At the same time it is moving through space on an annual journey round the Sun. One of the oddities about our planet is the fact that the axis upon which it spins is not perpendicular to the Earth's orbit around the Sun. Instead, it is inclined at an angle of 23½° from the vertical.

A 'year' is the time the spinning Earth takes to complete one orbit of the Sun. But there are different kinds of years. A *tropical year* is the time the Earth takes to move from one equinox back to the same equinox, or from one solstice back to the same solstice. The equinoxes are the two points in the Earth's orbit where the tilt of the Earth is sideways on to the Sun, and day and night are of equal length in all places. The solstices are the two points in the Earth's orbit where the North Pole points either directly towards, or directly away from, the Sun, producing the longest days and shortest nights, or *vice versa*, depending upon the hemisphere.

The *sidereal year*, however, describes the time taken by the Earth to orbit the Sun and come back to

The axis of the spinning globe describes a double cone as it precesses in the opposite direction to the spin of the Earth. It takes approximately 25,800 years to complete one revolution. This diagram ignores the wavy effects of nutation.

16

Right: **Diagrams showing the effect of the precession of the Earth's axis upon the seasons according to the sidereal year.**

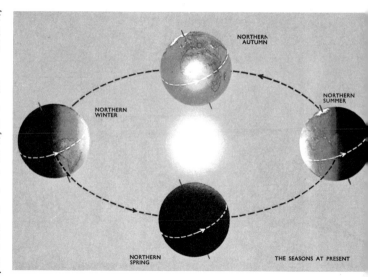

its original starting point as measured by the stars. As early as 125 B.C. the Greek astronomer Hipparchus noticed that the two intervals of time are not the same, the tropical year being about 20 minutes shorter than the sidereal year. In other words, the position of the equinoxes does not remain fixed among the stars, but 'precedes' the expected time. The reason for the *precession of the equinoxes* is the precession of the Earth's axis. If we think of the centre of the Earth as fixed, then the north-south axis moves slowly round in the opposite direction to the spin of the Earth to sweep out a double cone. All the time it maintains a constant, yet tilted, angle of 23½° from the vertical. The axis takes about 25,800 years to complete one circle, and though this may seem a long time it means that the North Pole (as fixed in the Earth) moves about 10 feet each day. At present, one end of the Earth's axis (the North Pole) points almost directly to *Polaris*, the Pole Star. In the year A.D. 2000 it will point *directly* at *Polaris*. In the year A.D. 14000 V*ega* will be the star directly above the North Pole, and in about A.D. 28000 *Polaris* will be the Pole Star once again.

The circle the Earth's axis describes, however, is by no means perfect. Instead, it follows a wavy curve through space. This second effect is called *nutation* and always occurs with precession. A spinning top provides an example of both precession and nutation. It rarely spins upright but usually at an angle and its tilted axis

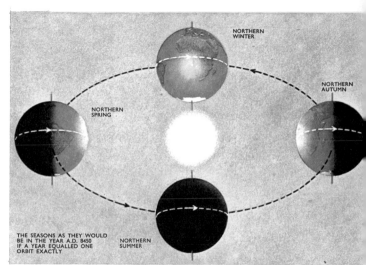

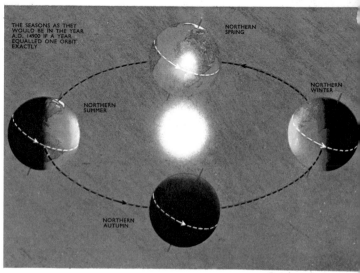

describes a slow irregular circle. But the precession of the Earth's axis has a different cause from the precession of the spinning top's axis. In the latter case a twisting force or *couple* is caused by the weight of the top acting downwards and the equal upward reaction of the floor. The upward reaction is trying to turn the top away from the upright position. The Earth is also caused to precess by a twisting force but one which is produced by different means from that operating on the top. The Earth bulges at the equator but owing to the inclination of the axis this bulge does not lie in the plane of the Earth's orbit round the Sun. Hence, the gravitational attraction of the Sun tries to pull the bulge into line with the

orbital plane and the gravitational attraction of the Moon produces a similar effect. This is the twisting force which causes the Earth's axis to precess in the opposite direction to the spin of the Earth. Although it is far smaller than the Sun, the Moon plays a greater part in producing the twisting force on the Earth, just as it plays the greatest part in creating tides, for gravitational attraction depends not only on the mass of two objects but also their distance apart, and the Moon is much nearer to the Earth than the Sun is (239,000 miles compared with 93,000,000 miles).

The Moon is also responsible for the complicating motion of nutation. In the first place, the Moon's orbit around the Earth is in a different plane to the Earth's orbit around the Sun, and in the second place, the Moon's orbit does not stay fixed in relation to the Earth. In fact, a line drawn perpendicular to the Moon's orbit would precess just like the Earth's axis, though it would complete one revolution in just over 18 years. This means that the effect of the Moon's pull on the Earth changes from year to year, and it is these variations which cause the fluctuations in the otherwise smooth precession of the Earth's axis.

The precession of the Earth's axis and the consequent precession of the equinoxes means that in just under 13,000 years' time the seasons will be reversed owing to the opposite tilt of the Earth's axis. Or rather they would be reversed according to the stars. If we measured by the sidereal year, which represents one true orbit, the Southern hemisphere would be having its seasons at the same time of the year that the Northern hemisphere does now and *vice versa.*

The axis of a spinning top precesses like the axis of the spinning Earth. But there is one important difference between them. In the case of the top the axis precesses in the same direction as the spin. With the Earth precession takes place in the opposite direction to the spin. This is because the twisting forces acting upon them are opposite.

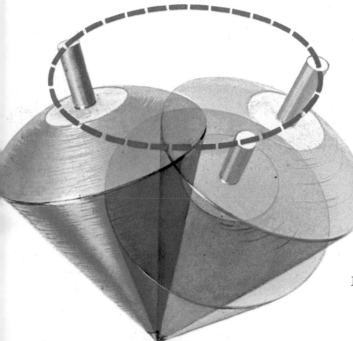

The side of
the Moon which
faces the Earth.

CHAPTER FOUR

The Moon

SIX OF THE nine major planets are known to hold smaller planetary bodies (satellites or moons) under the influence of their strong gravitational attraction. But the Earth's Moon holds a somewhat unique position in the solar system. It is the only satellite which is anywhere near the size of the parent planet. The diameter of the Moon (2,160 miles) is over one-quarter that of the Earth (7,926 miles). Other satellites of a comparable size (there are only five larger) all belong to the giant planets (Jupiter, Saturn, Uranus and Neptune) and are quite insignificant compared to them. Titan, for instance, the largest satellite, has a diameter of 3,500 miles,

19

The far side of the Moon. A map based on photographs taken by the Russian automatic interplanetary station, Lunik 3, launched in October 1959.

but the planet to which it belongs, Saturn, has a diameter of over 75,000 miles.

The Moon is the Earth's closest constant companion in space. On the average it is just 239,000 miles away and, although this may seem a considerable distance, it is a mere stone's throw in an astronomical sense. If it took a rocket one day to travel to the Moon, it would take it over a year to reach the Sun travelling at the same speed.

To circle the Earth, the Moon takes 27.32 days and it takes exactly the same time to spin upon its axis. In other words there is a part of its surface which can never be seen directly from the Earth. But tilting effects, collectively termed *librations*, mean that, all told, four-sevenths of the surface become visible during one orbit rather than just a half. The Moon itself rotates upon its axis at an absolutely constant rate but it does not move around the Earth at a constant speed, for the path it follows is not perfectly circular. The Moon moves fastest when it is nearest the Earth and slowest when it is farthest away. During its monthly journey, therefore, the orbital position and the axial position get slightly out of step and the Moon presents a slightly changing face to the Earth. In other words it is possible to peer a little way around alternate edges of the Moon. This is one tilting effect. Another is that the Moon's path around the Earth is inclined at a few degrees to its equator. So at one part of the month it is possible to see just over the Moon's north pole, while a fortnight later it is possible to see just under its south pole.

Since the Moon has a much smaller mass than the Earth (it would take 81 Moons to balance the Earth) it also has a smaller gravitational attraction. In fact the Moon's surface gravity is only one-sixth that of the Earth. The implications of this should prove interesting to lunar visitors. It will be possible to throw a ball almost half a mile, to jump many feet in the air and to pick up seemingly impossible loads.

Small as it is, the gravitational

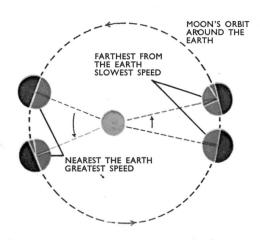

MOON'S ORBIT AROUND THE EARTH

FARTHEST FROM THE EARTH SLOWEST SPEED

NEAREST THE EARTH GREATEST SPEED

Due to its varying orbital speed it is possible to see around alternate 'edges' of the Moon.

attraction of the Moon is very noticeable on the Earth, for this is the chief cause of our tides.

Another consequence of the Moon's weak 'pull' is the fact that it does not possess an atmosphere. It was unable to hold down the air which may once have surrounded it and the gases simply leaked off into space. The fact that the Moon is airless (or almost so) shows up quite clearly during an *occultation*, i.e. when it passes in front of a star. The star continues to shine quite clearly until it suddenly disappears behind the Moon's bulk. If the Moon did have an atmosphere the star would flicker and fade before finally disappearing.

Lacking an atmospheric shield, the Moon has a far greater range of surface temperatures than anything experienced on the Earth. Day temperatures exceed 100° C. along its equator, while at night it is far colder than Antarctica in mid-winter (a lunar 'day' lasts for about two Earthly weeks, as does the lunar night').

For thousands of years the Moon has been known to be connected with the tides on Earth – the regular ebb and flow of the ocean waters on the margins of the continents. Long ago, it was noticed that the highest tides

occurred when the Moon was new, or when it was full, and that the lowest tides coincided with the quarter and three-quarter phases of the Moon. But the connection between them was all rather mysterious until Newton revolutionised scientific thought in the seventeenth century.

Making use of earlier observations and theories, Newton explained the universe in terms of gravity. Gravity is a force of attraction between masses. Every object attracts every other object but the force of attraction depends upon the masses of the objects and their distance apart. With immense bodies such as planets and stars this is a tremendous force. It prevents the Earth from flying away from the Sun and the Moon from flying away from the Earth.

If no other force were involved, the gravitational force between the Sun and the Earth would cause the Earth to spiral inwards and collide with the Sun. But there is another force – one which balances the inward acting force of gravity. This is called *centrifugal force* and it acts outwards on all bodies revolving about a point.

However, though bodies appear balanced and do not change their orbits as they revolve around one an-

The overall attractive force of the Moon is balanced by the Earth's centrifugal force.

MOON   EARTH

GRAVITATIONAL FORCE ACTING TOWARDS THE MOON

CENTRIFUGAL FORCE (DUE TO ROTATION OF EARTH AND MOON ABOUT A POINT) ACTS IN THE OPPOSITE DIRECTION

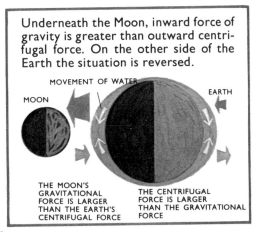

Underneath the Moon, inward force of gravity is greater than outward centrifugal force. On the other side of the Earth the situation is reversed.

MOVEMENT OF WATER

MOON   EARTH

THE MOON'S GRAVITATIONAL FORCE IS LARGER THAN THE EARTH'S CENTRIFUGAL FORCE

THE CENTRIFUGAL FORCE IS LARGER THAN THE GRAVITATIONAL FORCE

21

WM. F. LAMAN PUBLIC LIBRARY   145423
CIVIC CENTER
NORTH LITTLE ROCK, ARKANSAS

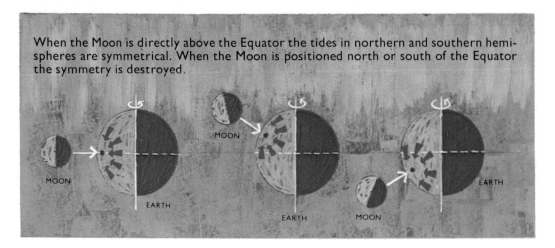

When the Moon is directly above the Equator the tides in northern and southern hemispheres are symmetrical. When the Moon is positioned north or south of the Equator the symmetry is destroyed.

other, individual particles at the surface are not in equilibrium. The gravitational pull on particles on the Earth increases the nearer the particles are to the Moon or to the Sun (the planets are too small or too far away to have any noticeable effect).

The more massive (denser) land is subjected to two and a half times the force exerted upon the waters. But land is solid and is not very elastic. Though it can be shown to move slightly by using delicate instruments, the movement cannot be detected with the eye. Water, on the other hand, flows easily, and as Newton explained in his book *The Principia* (published in 1687) it is movement under the influence of gravity that causes the tides.

The Moon is only 239,000 miles from the Earth and its attraction (rather than the Sun's) is the most important tide-raising force. Newton found the easiest way to demonstrate his theory was by imagining the world completely covered with a uniform layer of water.

The strongest pull upon this water will take place directly beneath the Moon. Here, the gravitational force of the Moon is greatest and a piling up of the water occurs at this point. On the other side of the Earth (furthest away from the Moon) centrifugal force caused by the revolving Earth is greater than the attractive force of gravity and water tends to flow away from the Moon.

But the Earth and the Moon are in constant movement so that the points on the Earth's surface towards which water moves are continuously changing. The Earth rotates once every 24 hours; the Moon revolves about the Earth once every 28 days. Therefore the Moon will appear to pass over the same line of longitude in 24 hours + 1/28 of 24 hours. This interval worked out to be 24 hours and 50 minutes. High tides will occur at a

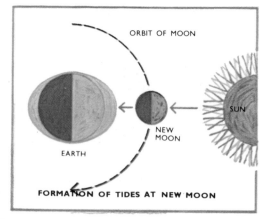

FORMATION OF TIDES AT NEW MOON

22

certain place every 12 hours 25 minutes (when the Moon is nearest and furthest away from that place).

A fact which complicates . lunar tides is that the Moon does not remain in the sky directly above the Equator. Instead, because of the tilt of the Earth's axis, it appears to move 28° north and south of the Equator. The levels of alternating high tides may vary accordingly.

The Sun, though 25 million times more massive than the Moon, is 93 million miles away from the Earth. Its gravitational pull is only about half that of the Moon and is not such an important tide-raising force by itself. But the Sun's position relative to the Moon and the Earth is continually changing. When the Sun and Moon are almost in line with the Earth (indicated by new and full moons), their gravitational forces combine and they produce the excessively high *spring tides*. The strongest spring tides occur at each Equinox (March 21st and September the 21st) when the Sun, Moon and Earth are directly in line. When the Sun is at right angles to the Earth and the Moon (indicated by the quarter and three-quarter phase of the Moon) the Sun's action is directly opposed to the Moon's and the very low *neap tides* occur.

The very high Spring tides take place when Sun, Moon and Earth are in a straight line. Lower neap tides occur when the action of the Sun is opposed to that of the Moon.

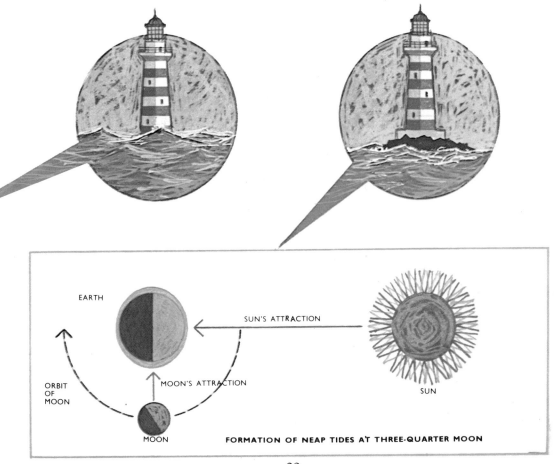

FORMATION OF NEAP TIDES AT THREE-QUARTER MOON

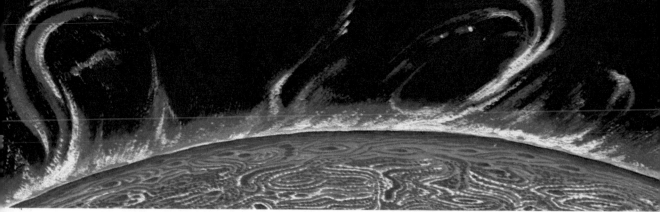

The Sun's surface is continually in motion, and great flares of luminous gas leap outward. These prominences are really only visible during an eclipse.

CHAPTER FIVE

The Sun

THE SUN, the star around which all of the planets in our solar system revolve, is a luminous mass of intensely hot gases, more than 300,000 times as heavy as the Earth and over 1,000,000 times as large. It is in fact our nearest star, though 'nearest' means that it is still 93,000,000 miles away from the Earth on the average (the Earth's path round the Sun is elliptical). The Sun is practically our only source of light and heat; without it, life as we know it would be impossible. Strangely enough, much the same elements are contained in the Sun as in the Earth and other planets, though in very different proportions. More than 99% of the Sun is made up of hydrogen and helium (with at least ten times as much of the former as the latter) but both of these elements are extremely rare on Earth as gases.

The surface of the Sun is obviously exceedingly hot; the actual temperature is around 6,000° C. (about twice the temperature of the filament of an electric lamp). But it is even hotter at the centre where the temperature may reach 20,000,000° C. The amount of heat produced by the Sun is tremendous. Considering that the heat spreads out equally in all directions, the share received by the Earth is 0·000000000005%, yet we may well be glad on a very hot summer's day that the percentage is no higher. This immense amount of heat is generated by nuclear reactions.

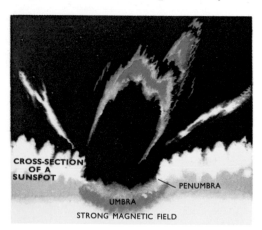

CROSS-SECTION OF A SUNSPOT

PENUMBRA

UMBRA

STRONG MAGNETIC FIELD

Strong magnetic fields deprive part of the Sun's surface of its supply of heat. The result is a cooler, darker region — a sunspot.

In the central 'power house' of the Sun hydrogen atoms are continually combining to produce atoms of a heavier gas—helium. Each time an atom of helium is formed, energy in the form of light and heat is released —this is what makes the Sun 'shine'.

In order to produce the amount of heat that the Sun does, some 600,000,000 tons of hydrogen must be converted into helium each *second*. The Sun has been doing this for at least 5,000,000,000 years but its bulk is so great that no more than 5% of its hydrogen has been used up. So there is no danger of the Sun running out of fuel for many many millions of years to come.

The visible part of the Sun, the intensely bright sphere of white light, is called the *photosphere*. From time to time dark patches, anything up to 50,000 miles in diameter, appear upon it. These are *sunspots* and represent areas of comparatively low temperature (4,000° C. instead of 6,000° C.).

Surrounding the photosphere is the *chromosphere*, a rarefied envelope of crimson gas which can be seen clearly only at a total eclipse (when the Moon passes directly between the Earth and the Sun). Great flares of luminous gas, normally invisible against the brightness of the Sun, leap many thousands of miles out from the chromosphere from time to time. These *solar prominences* are thought to be linked with sunspots. Beyond the chromosphere is the *corona*,- a pearly-white halo of extremely rare-fied gases, which, once again, becomes visible only during a total eclipse.

Like the Earth and most other celestial bodies, the Sun does not remain still but spins on its axis. The period taken to complete one revolution at the Sun's equator is about 25

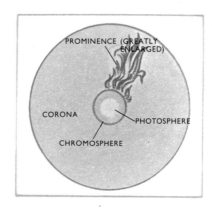

Earth days, but since the Sun is not a solid body, all parts of it do not revolve in unison. Near the Sun's poles one complete revolution takes 34 days.

Though to us the Sun is by far the largest and brightest object in the sky, when compared to the rest of the Universe it becomes far less awe-inspiring. The Sun is neither bright nor dim as stars go. There are stars which are many thousands of times as bright as our own and there are stars which are too dim to be seen.

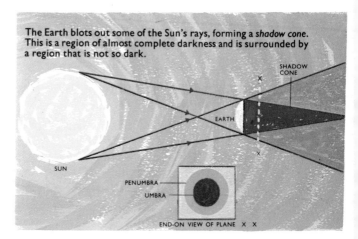

The Earth blots out some of the Sun's rays, forming a *shadow cone*. This is a region of almost complete darkness and is surrounded by a region that is not so dark.

An eclipse of the Sun. Occasionally the Moon orbiting round the Earth will blot out the Sun's rays, causing an eclipse in some corners of the world.

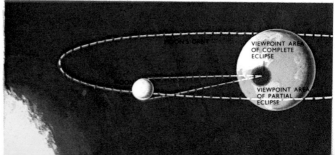

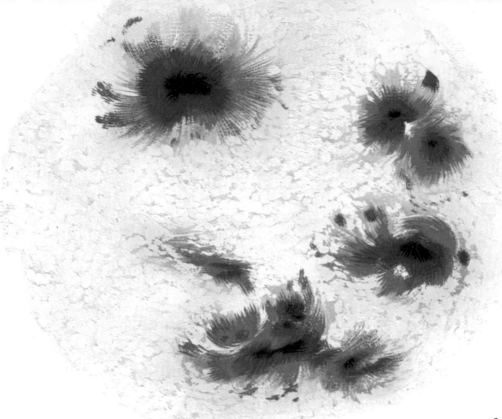

The darker region of the sunspot, the umbra, is surrounded by a less dark region, the penumbra, and enveloped by wisps of hotter gas. Sunspots occur mainly in pairs, in definite belts (right).

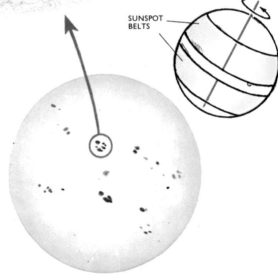

SUNSPOT BELTS

Every 11·1 years the Sun goes through a period of maximum sunspot activity. Midway between these maxima, the Sun might appear without sunspots. Then spots start to appear in narrow zones at latitudes of 35° north and south of the Sun's equator. The spots grow more numerous, and the zones in which they occur gradually move towards the equator. Their number passes through its maximum, and dies down as they get within 8° of the equator. Almost immediately a crop of spots marking the start of the next sunspot cycle appears at latitudes 35° north and south.

A sunspot is a dark patch on the Sun's surface. The central part, or *umbra*, is surrounded by a not so dark part, the *penumbra*. The sunspot appears dark because it is 1,500-2,000° C. colder than the rest of the surface (which is at about 6,000° C).

The reasons for the regular sunspot cycle are not known. The spot itself is probably caused by *magnetic* disturbances.

26

The Sun's core is a vast thermo-nuclear power-house. It produces energy which is carried outwards from the core into space. Much of the heat is carried out to the visible surface of the Sun, the *photosphere*, in convection currents, as streams of intensely hot gas are pushed outwards and bubble over the surface.

The gas is mainly hydrogen, and most of it will be ionized (electrons have been stripped off the atoms). The particles are therefore electrically charged, and their flow is akin to an electric current. Whenever an electric current flows, an electromagnetic field is set up around it. Similarly, an electromagnetic field is set up around the convection currents. Sometimes the electromagnetic field may get twisted, become particularly large, and repel the outward flow of the convection current. Heat is prevented from reaching the surface, which cools, appears darker and forms a sunspot. Strong magnetic fields have been detected around sunspots.

Single sunspots are rarely seen. They usually occur in pairs or in large clusters. The magnetic fields from a sunspot pair act in opposite directions, one behaving like a north magnetic pole and the other like a south magnetic pole.

Sunspots exist for about 20 days before disappearing. As the Sun rotates, they appear to move across the Sun's disc. Sunspot movement was the first method of measuring the rate of rotation of the Sun.

Sunspots appear in disturbed parts of the surface, and several other events may accompany them. Outward-flowing gases may be expelled right away from the Sun. They radiate an abnormal amount of ultra-violet light and X-radiation, which, on reaching the Earth's atmosphere, cause a sudden failure in short-wave radio communication. About four days later, the expelled gases themselves reach the Earth, where they cause magnetic storms and, in the upper atmosphere, Polar Aurorae.

THE SPECTRUM OF SUNLIGHT SHOWING THE MOST PROMINENT ABSORPTION LINES

Spectral Analysis

One of Newton's greatest discoveries was the fact that white light is really a mixture of coloured light. He found that when he placed a prism in the path of a beam of sunlight streaming through a hole in a blind into a darkened room, a band of colours was produced on a screen placed behind the prism. This band of colours (it includes every colour in the rainbow) is called the visible spectrum. A prism splits up light entering it because it refracts (bends) the coloured components by various amounts.

When an atom is 'excited' (e.g. by raising its temperature) it gives off light, and if this light is passed through a prism it is spread out into a range of colours. If the beam of light is first passed through a sufficiently narrow slit the overlapping of colours is prevented and a whole system of spectral lines is produced which together make up a spectrum. Each element gives off light with its own characteristic spectrum, so that by examining the spectrum produced by some unknown substance it is possible to identify the elements in it. For instance, the light given off by heated sodium atoms consists of simply two lines in the yellow portion of the spectrum. This method of investigation, called spectral analysis, can be applied to the Sun and stars because elements when cold absorb the light they emit when heated. The spectrum of light which has passed through sodium vapour shows two *black* lines close together in the yellow portion of the spectrum. The spectrum of sunlight (which is produced near the centre of the Sun and contains all colours) is crossed by a number of dark lines. These correspond to various elements in the outer parts of the Sun which are not hot enough to emit light and have, instead, absorbed the missing colours. So, by examining these absorption lines it is possible to determine which elements are present in the outer parts of the Sun.

CHAPTER SIX

Mercury — Frozen by the Sun

THE PLANET closest to the Sun is Mercury. It is much smaller than the Earth, measuring only some 3,100 miles across. It used to be thought that Mercury took the same time to rotate upon its axis as it takes to circle the Sun. This would mean that the planet always presented the same

The planet Mercury.

face to the Sun (just as we only ever see one side of the Moon).

Recent information, however, from the world's largest radio telescope in Puerto Rico has shown that the planet rotates faster than was previously thought — about once every 50 Earth days. A Mercurian year, on the other hand, lasts for 88 Earth days, or between 1½ and 2 Mercurian days.

The surface temperature of Mercury varies enormously. During the long Mercurian day it rises to 370°C. (hot enough to melt lead) while during the long night it falls far below freezing point.

The planet has no real atmosphere, only traces of gases, particularly carbon dioxide. The landscape is bleak and rugged, seared with jagged mountains, lifeless deserts and rocky plains. The difficulties of examining it from Earth are considerable, partly because it never comes closer to our planet than 50 million miles, and partly because it is the smallest of the major planets in the Solar System (3,100 miles in diameter). From time to time (1970, 1973 and 1986, for instance) it can be seen to cross the Sun; this is known as the Transit of Mercury. Mercury's axis is not tilted to the plane of its orbit like the Earth's, so the planet does not have seasons.

Mercury travels faster through space than any other planet — over 100,000 miles per hour. But its speed varies considerably, for Mercury follows a very elliptical or egg-shaped path around the Sun (29,000,000 miles to 43,000,000 miles) and travels fastest when it is closest to the Sun.

MERCURY	
Distance from the Sun (million miles):	36
Diameter (miles):	3,100
Volume (Earth=1):	0·06
Mass (Earth=1):	0·06
Density (Water=1):	5·13
'Day': 50 days	'year': 88 days
Orbital speed (miles/sec.):	27·2
Escape velocity (miles/sec.):	2·6
Surface gravity (Earth=1):	0·27
Satellites in order of closeness:	none

CHAPTER SEVEN

Mysterious Venus

THE PLANET Venus is one of the most conspicuous objects of the evening or morning sky. When it is an 'evening star' it sets soon after the Sun. As a 'morning star' it rises before the Sun, and then gradually disappears as the sky lightens. During most of the night Venus is never seen. The reason is that Venus lies between the Sun and Earth. Its mean distance from the Sun is 67,200,000 miles, while that of the Earth is 92,960,000 miles, The position of its orbit means that Venus is never seen more than 48° east or west of the Sun. If Venus is east of the Sun, it sets after the Sun does, so is an 'evening star'. If Venus is west of the Sun, it sets before the Sun does (so cannot be seen in the evening) and rises before the Sun. It is then a 'morning star'.

Venus is not a star at all. Stars are heavenly bodies, like the Sun, which are exceedingly hot and emit light of their own. Venus is a planet, and it can be seen only because it reflects light from the Sun. It appears bright because, of all the planets, it reflects the greatest proportion of the light it receives from the Sun. Venus reflects three quarters of the light it receives, while as a comparison, the Earth reflects less than four tenths.

Although Venus approaches the Earth more closely than any of the other planets do, very little is known about it. No plains, mountain ranges or oceans can be seen, for Venus is surrounded by a dense layer of cloud which obscures all the details of the surface of the planet. Through even the most powerful telescopes, Venus appears uniformly bright. Only the

Is there life on Venus?

Venus is almost as big as the Earth (its diameter is 7,700 miles) and practically as dense. It can 'hold on' to its atmosphere, because its gravitational pull is almost as great as the Earth's.

All these factors make an Earth-like form of life feasible. But weighing against them are the intense heat of the surface and the lack of oxygen. One recent theory suggests that Venus is covered entirely by water, favouring an aquatic form of life. But this does not seem possible if the temperature is greater than the boiling point of water. On the face of it, life on Venus seems highly unlikely.

opaque atmosphere can be seen. When infra-red light from the planet is viewed, one or two darker blotches may appear. (Infra-red light is more penetrating than ordinary light, and may perhaps be able to get through the atmosphere). But these blotches are not permanent features, like hills or oceans, for they disappear within a few hours. They are probably caused by cloud movements.

During a recent close approach of Venus, radar waves were beamed at the planet's surface to find out, by studying the 'echo' of radar waves

VENUS

Distance from Sun (million miles):	67·2
Diameter (miles):	7,700
Volume (Earth=1):	0·92
Mass (Earth=1):	0·82
Density (Water=1):	4·86
'Day': 30 days (?) 'year': 224¾ days	
Orbital Speed (miles/sec.):	21·7
Escape Velocity (miles/sec.):	6·4
Surface gravity (Earth=1):	0·86
Satellites in order of closeness:	none

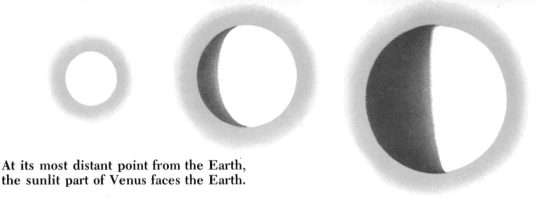

At its most distant point from the Earth, the sunlit part of Venus faces the Earth.

reflected back, whether the surface was mountainous or not. Results indicate that it is smoother than the Earth's surface.

Nothing definite is known about Venus' surface. Since it lies nearer the Sun than the Earth does, its surface is probably hotter than the Earth's. The 'greenhouse effect' of its atmosphere, too, would make surface temperatures high. The atmosphere lets through radiation from the Sun, but not that re-radiated back from the planet (the reason being that this is of longer wavelength). The atmosphere lets in the radiation, and then insulates the planet, preventing the radiation from getting away. A surface temperature of $200°$ or $300°$ C. (two or three times the boiling point of water) has been recorded using radio astronomy. More recent results suggest that it is even higher than this — about $400°$ C.

However, a little bit more is known about the visible part of Venus, its atmosphere. Each gas in the atmosphere absorbs certain wavelengths of light, and these wavelengths will be missing in the spectrum of the light from Venus. By studying the spectrum it has been found that carbon dioxide is the main constituent of the atmosphere. There is roughly 250 times as much carbon dioxide as there is at the surface of the Earth. Nitrogen may be present, but neither oxygen nor appreciable amounts of water vapour

have been detected by this method.

The absence of oxygen is probably caused by high temperatures on the planet. Under these conditions, oxygen would take part in chemical reactions, and become part of carbon dioxide.

The most recent information suggests that the clouds which perpetually mask the surface of Venus are not composed of water vapour, though what they are composed of remains a mystery. Some scientists have suggested an oily substance — possibly a kind of smog.

Recent results have also suggested that the clouds are only about 15 miles thick, far less than was previously thought. From observations of the shape of Venus a figure of 300 miles for the cloud layer had been obtained. For Venus has *phases* like the Moon. We see only the part of Venus which is facing the Sun, and, depending on the relative positions of Venus, Sun and Earth, this part may appear crescent shaped, 'new' or 'full'. The bright *cusps* of the crescent Venus may extend a considerable way around the darkened portion of the disc. The thickness of the atmosphere can be gauged by measuring how far round the cusps extend, for the extensions are caused by the atmosphere.

Measuring the rate of rotation

All the planets rotate on their axes. Observers on other planets could see quite easily that the Earth rotated, for they could follow the movement of the permanent land masses and oceans, and find that they reappeared in the same position once every 24 hours. But Venus has no such permanent visible features, and the rotation cannot be followed in this way.

Various estimates on the period of rotation have ranged from 24 hours to 225 days! The period was thought unlikely to be as long as 225 days, for this is the length of the 'year' on Venus. If Venus turned on its axis only once during each orbit of the Sun, then the same half of the planet would always point towards the Sun. One half would perpetually intercept the solar radiation, and be exceedingly hot, while the other would never receive solar radiation, and be perpetually cold.

In fact, the temperature of the dark half would approach Absolute Zero ($-273°$ C). The temperature of the atmosphere has been measured, and it is in fact far warmer than this — about $-25°$ C. This suggests that all parts of the planet do face the Sun for part of the time. But even so, the rotation period must be fairly slow for the

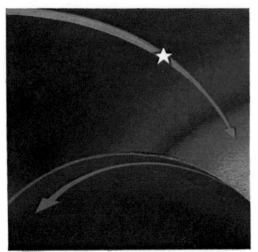

Venus is east of the Sun, and is an 'evening star'.

When Venus is west of the Sun, it is a 'morning star'.

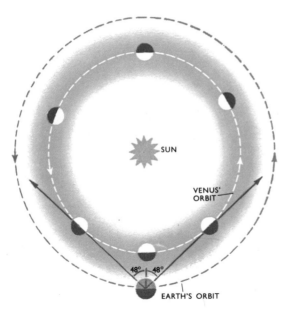

Venus never appears more than 48°E. or W. of the Sun. Because it lies between the Earth and the Sun, it has phases.

atmosphere to have cooled down to −25° C., in the planet's 'night'. (Daytime temperatures in the atmosphere are about 60° C.). If the period were as short as an Earth day, the temperature would not have dropped so much.

There is another reason why the 'day' on Venus cannot be as short as 24 hours. When a planet is rotating fairly quickly, the movement of one part towards the observer, and the movement of the other part away causes the *wavelengths* of radiation reflected by the planet to become either shorter or longer. Because the planet is moving, the waves of radiation have either been squashed in or pulled out. This is called the *Döppler Effect*. The quicker the rotation, the more noticeable the effect. But on Venus no Döppler Effect has been observed. The rotation must be too slow to cause a noticeable effect.

Many astronomers decided that a period of a few weeks, between the two extremes, was the most likely. However, an American space 'probe' passed within 21,600 miles of Venus in December, 1962, and its instruments indicated that the period was even longer than 225 days. If this is to be believed, then there must be strong winds circulating the planet to prevent the dark side from cooling down to Absolute Zero.

CHAPTER EIGHT

Mars—the Red Planet

IF LIFE EXISTS on any of the other planets of the Solar System, then the most likely home for it is the planet Mars. Venus and Mercury, the two inner planets, are too hot to support life. The outer planets, Jupiter, Saturn, Uranus, Neptune and Pluto, are all far too cold. Only on Mars are conditions even remotely similar to those on Earth, and there is strong evidence of life on the planet.

Martian life would probably be very different from terrestrial life. Mars is a small planet (its diameter is only about a half that of the Earth). Because it is smaller than the Earth, it exerts a smaller gravitational pull on its atmosphere, with the result that nearly all its atmospheric gases have long since escaped into space. So Mars has a very rarefied atmosphere, and very little oxygen, the gas essential to an Earth-like form of life. Added to this, Mars is an arid planet,

with practically no water, another substance necessary for life. Moreover, Martian nights are very cold indeed. Mars has almost no atmosphere to insulate it and keep in the heat received during the Martian day.

MARS

Distance from Sun (million miles):	141·5
Diameter (miles):	4,200
Volume (Earth=1):	0·15
Mass (Earth=1):	0·11
Density (Water=1):	3·96
'Day': 24 hr. 37 m.	'year': 687 days
Orbital speed (miles/sec.):	15
Escape velocity (miles/sec.):	3·1
Surface gravity (Earth=1):	0·37
Satellites in order of closeness:	Phobos, Deimos

All these factors would make life on Mars difficult. Also it has not been easy to collect evidence of life, for Mars is seldom in a favourable viewing position. It takes roughly two years to orbit the Sun. At its nearest point, it is only about 30 million miles away from the Earth. At this point Mars and Earth are said to be in *opposition*. But the Earth gets farther and

Each year the polar ice-caps melt and re-form. *Left:* **Mars in winter, with a prominent North Polar ice-cap.** *Right:* **how Mars appears three months later. Much of the ice-cap has already melted.**

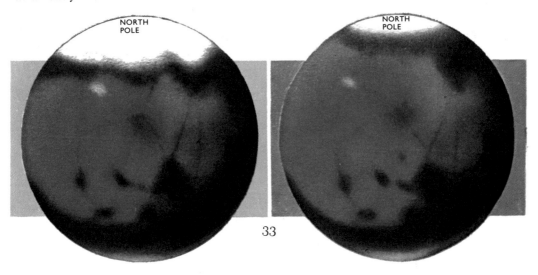

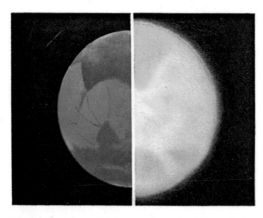

Photographs of Mars taken in blue light show up the atmosphere, while photographs taken in red light show the surface.

farther away from Mars, as it orbits the Sun in half the time Mars takes. By the time the Earth has completed one orbit, Mars has only reached the half-way of its orbit. The two planets are now at their greatest distance apart. Mars, hidden behind the Sun, is then practically invisible.

The Earth completes another orbit and, at about the same time, Mars completes her first orbit. Mars and the Earth are near each other once more, two years and two months after their last nearest point, or *opposition*. Only at times of opposition can de-

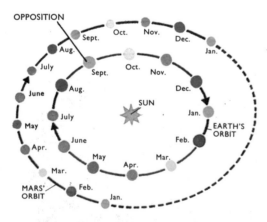

Mars is close to the Earth (in *opposition*) only once every two years.

tailed studies of the planet be made.

Most of the features of Mars' surface remain, like the seas and mountains of the Earth, fixed from season to season. Dark patches on the surface were once mistaken for oceans, but this was disproved when it was found that Mars was an exceptionally dry planet. Most of the rest of the surface has a reddish tint. This is thought to be arid desert, of dust rather than sand, and ice-cold most of the time.

One prominent feature of Mars does, however, change with the seasons. Like the Earth, Mars has two poles, marked by white polar ice-caps. But these are thought to be only thin layers of hoar-frost about an inch thick. As Mars orbits the Sun, first one pole, then the other is nearer the Sun, giving rise to four seasons, as on the Earth (only each season is twice as long on Mars). In the Martian summer-time, the frost melts, and it is thought that water from the pole flows towards the equator. The entire ice-cap may disappear.

The ice-caps are, in fact, the only sources of water on Mars. As the melted ice reaches some of the darker areas of the surface, they seemingly change, turning from brown or lilac to a greenish colour. They are apparently revived by the arrival of the water. For this reason, plants are thought to be growing on these areas. They may be like mosses or lichens, and they must be hardy to survive extremes of temperature on Mars. At noon on Mars' equator, the temperature may reach 25° C. (77° F.) but during the night it may drop to −40° C. (−40° F.).

When the seasons change once more, and the polar ice-cap returns, it is thought that the plants, drained of their moisture, die down and remain dormant until they are revived by the

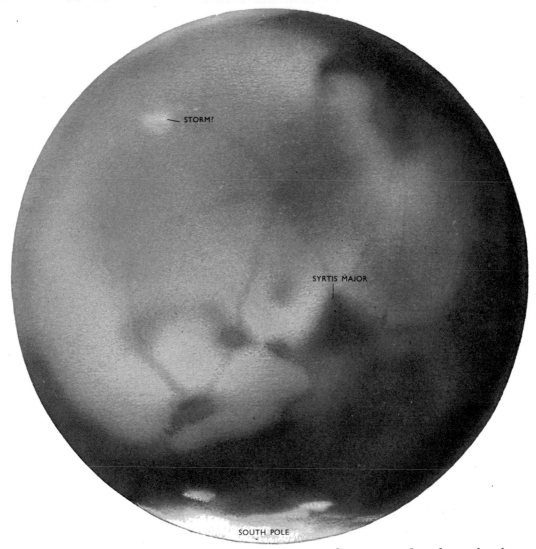

STORM?

SYRTIS MAJOR

SOUTH POLE

next arrival of polar water.

There are other pointers which suggest that the dark greenish areas are caused by a plant-like kind of life. Plants on Earth absorb a certain wavelength of light in the infra-red part of the spectrum, and this wavelength is therefore absent in the light reflected by the plants. By examining the light received from Mars (this is light, coming originally from the Sun, which is reflected by the planet) astronomers have been able to detect a similar absorption of infra-red light of practically the same wavelength. This particular wavelength is lacking in the light reflected by Mars. It has been absorbed by the dark greenish areas.

Another piece of evidence has been gleaned from examining the ultra-violet light reflected by Mars. Although Mars' atmosphere is very scant (even at the surface, the atmosphere is thinner than the atmosphere at the top of Mount Everest), it does provide some protection against harmful ultra-violet light coming from the Sun. The atmosphere absorbs much of the ultra-violet light, and prevents it from reaching the surface. But sometimes the atmosphere is disrupted, and the ultra-violet light gets through. Occurrences of this kind can be detected by examining the ultra-violet light reflected by Mars. If the season is suitable, and the ultra-violet absorbing atmosphere is there, then

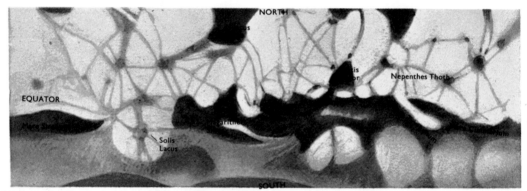

Maps of Mars can be built up from the results of many observations. The Martian canals are shown by close inspection to be very irregular markings.

the dark areas spread. The plants are flourishing. When the atmosphere is disrupted, the dark areas lighten again, and contract. The interpretation of this is that the plants have been killed by bombardment with ultra-violet light.

Leading out from the dark patches of 'vegetation' are thin dark 'lines', appearing to criss-cross the surface. Earlier astronomers imagined in the dark 'lines' far more regularity than they could actually see. They considered that the lines, or *canals*, could have been produced only by an intelligent population. The canals had been built to take water from the polar regions to irrigate the dry regions near the Equator. The amount

of water on Mars is, however, only enough to fill one river, and scarcely enough to supply a complicated network of canals. With more powerful telescopes, it can be seen that the 'canals' are not regular at all. They may be borders between areas of slightly different brightness, or specks of volcanic dust which stand out clearly against the red of the desert.

Mars has been examined in fair detail from the Earth. The next step is the making of observations on Mars itself, landing sampling rockets on the Martian surface to probe it. The instruments carried by the rockets would be able to analyse the 'vegetation', and transmit information about it back to interpreters on Earth.

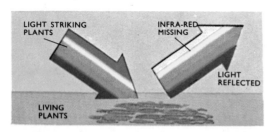

Vegetation on Earth is known to absorb some infra-red light. So this light is missing in the light reflected by the plants. Absorption of infra-red has been detected in light reflected by the greenish areas of Mars.

Vegetation can be killed by exposing it to ultra-violet radiation. The atmosphere stops most of the ultra-violet. When Mars' atmosphere is disrupted, the ultra-violet gets through, and the greenish areas turn to brown.

CHAPTER NINE

Giant Jupiter

THE FOUR inner planets of the Solar System—Mercury, Venus, Earth and Mars, were all formed in a similar fashion. They have dense, rocky, mainly solid cores surrounded by as much atmosphere as the planet has managed to keep.

Outside the inner planets is a belt of smaller lumps of rocky matter, the asteroids, and beyond the asteroids lie the huge major planets. Their structure is believed to be very different from the structure of the inner planets. Some astronomers believe that they have no rocky core at all. They are intensely cold, and the only solid parts of the planet may be frozen ammonia and methane, and hydrogen compressed under such immense gravitational forces that it is almost like a solid metal.

Jupiter is by far the largest planet of the Solar System. Its diameter is 86,800 miles—over 10 times the Earth's diameter—and its mass is 2½ times greater than the masses of all the rest of the planets put together.

Mainly because of its huge size, Jupiter is one of the most conspicuous objects in the sky. It is so bright that early astronomers thought it must be hot, like the Sun and the stars, producing its own light. Since then it has been found that Jupiter is a cold planet. The bright light coming from Jupiter is sunlight, reflected by its surface.

The outermost layers of the atmosphere of Jupiter consist of hydrogen with some methane and ammonia. Floating in it are clouds of crystallized ammonia at a temperature of about

$-150°$ C. It is the clouds of ammonia which reflect light and are seen. They hide the rest of the planet, so what lies underneath is still a matter of speculation. One theory suggests that a layer

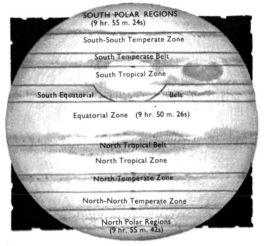

SOUTH POLAR REGIONS
(9 hr. 55 m. 24s)
South-South Temperate Zone
South Temperate Belt
South Tropical Zone
South Equatorial   Belt
Equatorial Zone   (9 hr. 50 m. 26s)
North Tropical Belt
North Tropical Zone
North Temperate Zone
North-North Temperate Zone
North Polar Regions
(9 hr. 55 m. 42s)

Parts of the surface spin round more quickly than others. This indicates that the visible surface cannot be solid.

Analysing the Atmosphere

The only way of telling what elements are present on Jupiter is to examine the light reflected by its surface. This light comes in the first place from the Sun. Most of it is reflected by the atmosphere, but certain colours, or *wavelengths* may be absorbed by atoms and molecules in the atmosphere. These wavelengths will therefore be missing in the light reflected back towards the Earth. Missing wavelengths can be detected by splitting the light up into its spectrum. Missing bands of colour indicate that hydrogen, methane and ammonia are present.

SOUTH TROPICAL BELT

NORTH TROPICAL BELT

The colours of Jupiter are probably caused by dissolved metals, absorbing light. Recently the North and South tropical belts appear to have merged together.

of ice 16,000 miles thick covers a solid centre. According to another theory, there is no division between atmosphere and core. The hydrogen becomes denser and denser nearer the centre, compressed by the gravitational forces of attraction.

Only the atmosphere of Jupiter can be seen. Nevertheless, it has several interesting features. On the disc, running parallel to the Equator, are dark and light belts, greenish and brown in colour. The different colours are believed to be caused by metals such as sodium and calcium, dissolved in the liquid ammonia. The belts are currents in the atmosphere, started by the planet's rotation.

JUPITER

Distance from Sun (million miles):	483·3
Diameter (miles):	86,800
Volume (Earth=1):	1,312
Mass (Earth=1):	318·4
Density (Water=1):	1·34
'Day': 9 hr. 50 m.	'year': 11·86 years
Orbital speed (miles/sec.):	8·1
Escape velocity (miles/sec.):	37
Surface gravity (Earth=1):	2·64
Satellites in order of closeness:	Amalthea, Io, Europa, Ganymede, Callisto.
(The outer seven are unnamed.)	

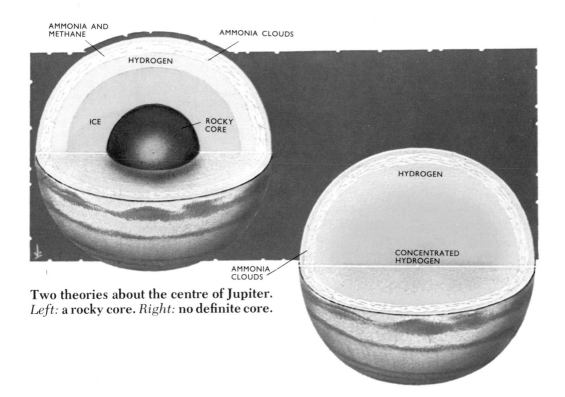

Two theories about the centre of Jupiter.
Left: a rocky core. *Right:* no definite core.

Jupiter rotates very quickly indeed, in less than 10 hours. The rotation causes surface details to move rapidly across the visible disc, and the period of rotation is measured by observing how quickly they move. The most conspicuous detail is the 'great red spot'. At one time it was 25,000 miles long and 8,000 miles across, but its size varies. The latitude of the spot varies up and down by 2 or 3 degrees, and its longitude also varies to and fro. Because the spot does not rotate at a constant speed it cannot be fixed to whatever surface there is. It is believed to be a solid mass of helium (containing metals that give it its reddish colour) floating in clouds of condensed gases. The spot does not always float at the same level in the atmosphere. When it is drawn towards the rest of the planet, the edges of it are obscured by ammonia clouds, and this explains why the size of the red spot varies.

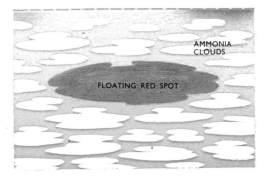

The apparent size of the red spot changes. It is thought to be a solid island of helium, floating at different levels in the atmosphere.

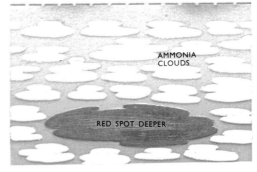

Various other spots in the belts are visible. By timing their movement, it is found that the belts do not rotate with exactly the same period. A 'day' at Jupiter's equator is shorter than a 'day' at Jupiter's poles. The equatorial 'day' lasts for 9 hours 50 minutes, while a 'day' near the poles lasts 9 hours 55 minutes. This all proves that the visible part of Jupiter is fluid. As a result of the quick rotation, the atmosphere bulges at the Equator. The planet appears noticeably flattened at the poles.

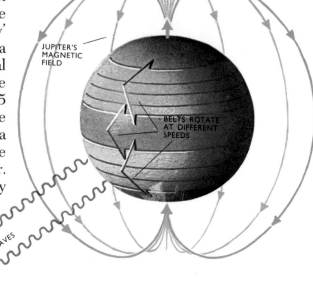

Radio waves from Jupiter may be caused by the varying speeds of rotation of the planet. These lead to powerful magnetic fields, and radio-wave emission. Alternatively they may be solar waves, distorted and reflected by Jupiter.

Jupiter sends out powerful radio waves at a frequency of around 22 million cycles per second. This is slightly lower than the frequency of radio waves carrying television transmissions, which start at about 45 million cycles per second. Many other objects in the sky are continuously emitting radio waves of about this frequency, but Jupiter can be distinguished by its very distinctive signal. When its radio waves are amplified by a radio receiver and turned into an audible sound, the noise is not unlike the sea surging to and fro on the shore. It comes in an irregular series of bursts.

No one knows for sure the source of these mysterious radio emissions. They are evidence in favour of a liquid core within the planet. Currents of charged particles flowing inside set up powerful magnetic fields (the Earth's magnetism may be caused by similar currents in the Earth's core). The magnetic fields vary because of the complicated nature of Jupiter's rotation — each belt rotates at a different speed. Radio waves are always emitted when magnetic fields are varying. There are many other theories to explain the radio waves, but not enough observational facts to prove any of them conclusively.

CHAPTER TEN

Saturn's Rings

SATURN has nine known moons. At one time it may have had ten moons, but the innermost moon broke into fragments, and now forms the system of rings around the planet. The nearest of the remaining moons, Mimas, is only 115,000 miles from the

SATURN

Distance from Sun (million miles):	886·2
Diameter (miles):	75,100
Volume (Earth=1):	763
Mass (Earth=1):	95·2
Density (Water=1):	0·71
'Day': 10 hr. 38 m.	'year': 29·46 years
Orbital speed (miles/sec.):	6
Escape velocity (miles/sec.):	22
Surface gravity (Earth=1):	1·17

Satellites in order of closeness: Mimas, Enceladus, Tethys, Dione, Rhea, Titan, Hyperion, Iapetus, Phoebe.

planet's centre. The distance between this moon and Saturn is less than the distance between the Earth and its own Moon (our moon is 239,000 miles away from Earth). But Saturn is much more massive than the Earth. Consequently, it exerts a bigger gravitational force, which pulls strongly on the surface of its moons. The tides on Earth are caused by a similar gravitational pull operating between the Earth and its Moon.

The gravitational pull would be even greater on a moon nearer Saturn's surface. If a moon had formed there, it could not have remained stable for very long. It broke up into myriads of tiny fragments, which spread out to form the rings of Saturn. Relatively tiny fragments, probably much less than a mile across, can exist where the much larger moon was unstable. The fragments now occupy a

ring system circling Saturn, 40,000 miles wide but only 10 miles thick.

Saturn is surrounded by a definite 'danger zone' in which large moons would be liable to break up. All the rings lie inside the danger zone, and all the moons lie outside it.

The bright section of the ring system is in three parts: the *outer ring*, the *inner ring* and the *crêpe ring*, lying inside the inner ring. The brightness of the rings is probably caused by a covering of hoar frost. This makes them efficient reflectors of light from the Sun.

In the spaces dividing the rings,

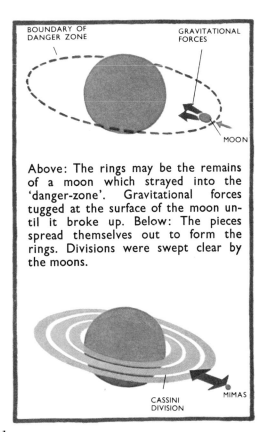

Above: The rings may be the remains of a moon which strayed into the 'danger-zone'. Gravitational forces tugged at the surface of the moon until it broke up. Below: The pieces spread themselves out to form the rings. Divisions were swept clear by the moons.

Saturn has a distinct bulge at the Equator. Pale belts run parallel to the Equator. The rings orbit the planet like individual moons.

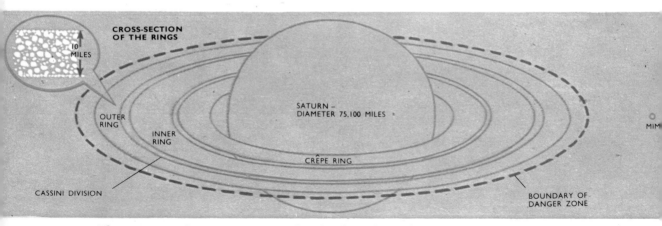

CROSS-SECTION OF THE RINGS

10 MILES

OUTER RING

INNER RING

SATURN – DIAMETER 75,100 MILES

CRÊPE RING

CASSINI DIVISION

BOUNDARY OF DANGER ZONE

MIM

The outer and inner rings are bright, but the crêpe ring is semi-transparent. The 'periods' of all the divisions are simple fractions of the period of one or more of Saturn's nine moons.

there are no fragments at all. The *Cassini* division separates the inner ring from the outer ring. It is about 3,000 miles wide. This region has been swept clean of fragments by the gravitational attraction of the moons, especially by Mimas. The matter orbiting Saturn goes regularly around the planet. It has a fixed period, the time it takes to complete one orbit. (Our Moon's period is one month.) If there were any fragments in the Cassini division, then it works out that their period would be exactly half the period of Mimas. Mimas has attracted each portion of the division

Saturn takes $29\frac{1}{2}$ years to complete one orbit of the Sun. Its appearance changes over the years, as the rings are seen at different angles.

Is Saturn a solid planet?

The surface of Saturn is almost certainly covered by swirling clouds of methane and ammonia, and its composition is similar to that of the neighbouring planet, Jupiter. But Saturn is farther away from the Sun than Jupiter, and it must be even colder. The clouds contain a smaller proportion of ammonia than on Jupiter, because more of it has frozen solid in the intense cold.

Underneath the cloud, it is so cold that there is bound to be some form of solid. This could be 'rocky', or it could be frozen hydrogen, compressed by pressures within the planet.

The composition of Saturn's atmosphere is found by examining the spectrum of light reflected by the visible part of the planet. But there is no way of finding the composition of the inner regions of the planet. However, the mass and the dimensions of the planet as a whole can be measured, and from this the density of the planet can be calculated. Saturn is the only planet which could float in water. Its density is very low indeed – being only 13% the density of the Earth – and its density is certainly lower than the density of any other planet. To account for this low density, at least half the planet must be made up of hydrogen (the lightest element).

Well-marked belts in the atmosphere run along the lines of latitude. But they are not so prominent as the belts of Jupiter. White spots appear on the surface from time to time – there are no stationary markings on the planet because the part of it which is visible is made up of cloud, and not attached to the surface.

Because the outer part of the planet is not solid, the rotation of Saturn on its axis has caused a large bulge at the Equator. Saturn spins round once every 10 hours 38 minutes.

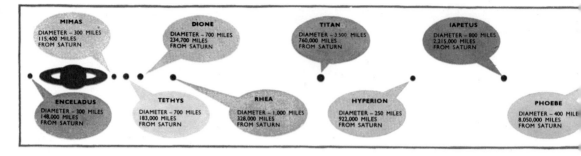

The moons of Saturn. The seven nearest moons orbit Saturn in roughly the same plane as the rings, and all except Phoebe orbit in the same direction. Phoebe may be a captured asteroid.

at regular intervals, and by doing so it has managed to pull all the fragments away from the division.

Two of Saturn's other moons have helped to form the Cassini division, because their periods are simple multiples of the period of the Cassini division. The period of *Enceladus,* another moon, is three times the period of the Cassini division. *Tethys,* a more remote moon, has four times the period of Cassini division.

It is no accident that the boundary between the inner ring and the crêpe has a period one third that of Mimas. The gap between the rings has been formed there because the periods of ring and moon are simply related.

Each particle in the rings keeps to its own orbit around the planet. The period of the particle increases with distance away from the planet, so the particles in the inner rings orbit Saturn more quickly than particles in the outer ring. This has been confirmed by examining light reflected by the rings. The change in the wavelength of light (the *Döppler* shift), a result of the movement of the rings towards and away from the observer, shows that different parts of the ring system are rotating at different speeds.

The brightest of the rings is the inner ring. The rings cast shadows in the sunlight striking the planet. The inner ring casts a sharp shadow, because it is opaque, and because it contains the most matter. Some light filters through the outer ring, showing that the fragments of matter are not so densely packed. The crêpe ring is semi-transparent.

CHAPTER ELEVEN

Uranus

URANUS IS another vast planet, about 29,000 miles in diameter. It orbits on average 1,783 million miles away from the Sun, taking 84 years to do so. It appears pale green when seen through a telescope. Uranus spins on its axis every 10¾ hours, an unusual feature being that the axis is tilted almost end-on to the plane of its path around the Sun. This means that sometimes the planet's north pole is seen from Earth as it moves round its orbit, sometimes the south pole is seen. Uranus has five moons, the largest of them being possibly 1,500 miles across. The planet was discovered in 1781 by the English astronomer William Herschel. He wanted to call it Georgium Sidus (star of King George III), but this name was rejected.

The main problem of observing Uranus is that it is so far away from us. It is likely, however, that it would be an impossible planet to visit, with temperatures around −190° C. and a poisonous methane atmosphere.

The strange tilt of the planet's axis means that the moons of Uranus follow a path almost at right angles to the plane of its orbit. When Uranus is presented 'end-on' to the Earth it is possible to see the complete orbits of its moons. When it is 'side-on' to the Earth the moons appear to climb up the side of the planet and disappear over the top.

In common with the other giant planets, Uranus is far less dense than the Earth, and despite its size it has a smaller gravitational pull.

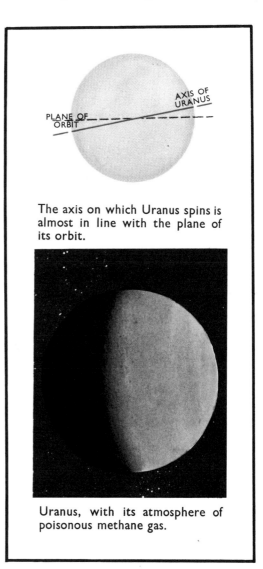

The axis on which Uranus spins is almost in line with the plane of its orbit.

Uranus, with its atmosphere of poisonous methane gas.

URANUS ♅

Distance from Sun (million miles):	1,783
Diameter (miles):	29,300
Volume (Earth=1):	64
Mass (Earth=1):	7
Density (Water=1):	1·26
'Day': 10 hr. 49 m.	'year': 84·01 years
Orbital speed (miles/sec.):	4·2
Escape velocity (miles/sec.):	14
Surface gravity (Earth=1):	0·92
Satellites in order of closeness: Miranda, Ariel, Umbriel, Titania, Oberon.	

CHAPTER TWELVE

Distant Neptune

NEPTUNE, THE last of the giant planets, was discovered in 1846, by the German astronomer Johann Galle. It was discovered as a result of apparent irregularities in the behaviour of Uranus which could be explained only by the presence of another planet. Every planet in the Solar System slows down or speeds up every other to some extent, but neighbouring planets have the greatest influence on each other.

Neptune has a diameter of 27,700 miles and is on average about 2,794 million miles from the Sun. As might be expected with an outer planet, it takes a long time to complete its orbit round the Sun, about 165 years. To spin once on its axis (which unlike that of Uranus is tilted at a fairly wide angle to the plane of orbit) takes Neptune about 15¾ hours. The day on Neptune is half as long again as on the other giant planets.

Neptune has two moons, Triton and Nereid. The first one orbits the planet from east to west about 220,000 miles out. The second circles Neptune at a mean distance of about 3,500,000 miles.

Neptune is so distant from Earth that it cannot be seen with the naked eye. Even through a telescope it appears only as a small green disk, with rather light bands round its equator and polar regions. The surface conditions are therefore a matter of conjecture rather than observed fact. One thing is certain; it is very cold there. Temperatures are in the region of −200° C. And even when the Sun is highest in the sky it can never be lighter than dusk on Earth. The Sun would appear as a distant star in the sky, overshadowed by the menacing bulk of the satellite Triton looming close overhead.

It has been suggested that the atmosphere is a poisonous mixture of methane, hydrogen and ammonia about 2,000 miles thick. Below may lie a layer of ice, 6,000 miles thick or more, covering a relatively small rock core.

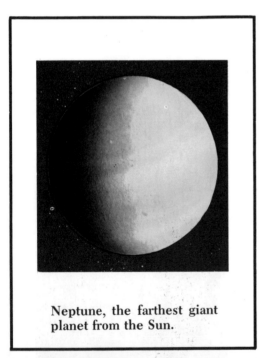

Neptune, the farthest giant planet from the Sun.

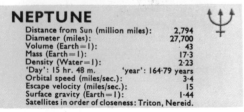

NEPTUNE

Distance from Sun (million miles):	2,794
Diameter (miles):	27,700
Volume (Earth=1):	·43
Mass (Earth=1):	17·3
Density (Water=1):	2·23
'Day': 15 hr. 48 m. 'year': 164·79 years	
Orbital speed (miles/sec.):	3·4
Escape velocity (miles/sec.):	15
Surface gravity (Earth=1):	1·44
Satellites in order of closeness: Triton, Nereid.	

CHAPTER THIRTEEN

Pluto—the outermost Planet

PLUTO IS the outermost known planet, some 3,670 million miles on average from the Sun. It is also the most recent of the major planetary bodies to be discovered. Pluto was predicted by the American astronomer Lowell in 1905. He said it would be about 4,000 million miles from the Sun, and that it would take about 282 years to complete one orbit. These predictions were based on irregularities in the movements of Neptune (then the outermost known planet) which could be explained only by the existence of such a planet.

Lowell started a systematic search for his planet X, but he did not live to discover it. That triumph only came in 1930 when Clyde Tombaugh photographed part of the night sky on successive nights and noticed a point of light which had moved considerably against the background. Pluto was found close to its predicted position but was less massive than had been expected.

Pluto has a diameter of 3,600 miles. It takes 248 years to circle the Sun. The spin around the axis is not known but may take a little under six and a half days. The most powerful telescopes show the planet as little more than a yellowish spot.

Since Pluto is so distant from us, little is known about it save the details mentioned. It is undoubtedly cold there, and the atmosphere is probably a dense mass of hydrogen and helium. Some astronomers believe that Pluto was not formed in the same way as the other planets but is really an escaped satellite of some other body, possibly Neptune. One of the reasons for this is that its orbit is very eccentric (i.e. uncircular), far more so than any of the other planets. So eccentric is the orbit, in fact, that it actually crosses that of its neighbour Neptune, and during these periods Pluto is nearer to the Sun than the much larger planet to which it possibly once belonged.

Another strange thing about Pluto's orbit is that it is inclined at 17° to the Earth's orbit, far more than any other planet's. All told, Pluto does not fit very well into the general pattern of the planets.

PLUTO

Distance from Sun (million miles):	3,670
Diameter (miles):	3,600
Volume (Earth = I):	?
Mass (Earth = I):	?
Density (Water = I):	?
'Day': 6 days 9 hr.	'year': 248·43 years
Orbital speed (miles/sec.):	?
Escape velocity (miles/sec.):	?
Surface gravity (Earth = I):	
Satellites in order of closeness:	none

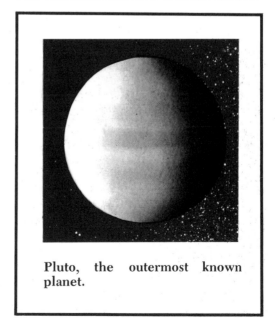

Pluto, the outermost known planet.

CHAPTER FOURTEEN

Meteors and Meteorites

MOVING AT 45 miles per second, a fragment of stone, no more than a millimetre in diameter, strikes the Earth's atmosphere. The friction of the stone against the atmospheric gases is intense. The tiny stone's surface begins to glow with heat. The result? A *meteor,* or *shooting star,* a bright line of fire which flashes momentarily across the skies.

Such fragments of stone are called *meteoroids.* Like the Earth, and other planets, meteoroids revolve in orbits about the Sun. A diameter of one millimetre is about average size. Some, a centimetre or so in diameter, produce exceptionally brilliant meteors. Very occasionally a 'giant' meteoroid—between 1 and 10 centimetres in diameter—strikes the

atmosphere, giving the spectacular 'fireballs', and a few—the so-called *bolides*—mark their entry by loud explosions.

Meteoroids are, of course, far too small to reflect sunlight like the Moon and the planets. Consequently, they can only be detected when they enter the Earth's atmosphere and become incandescent. The height at which they begin to glow is about 65 miles above the Earth's surface. Usually they are completely burnt out 50 miles up, and the trail of light ends abruptly. Very bright fireballs, however, may be visible down to fifteen or ten miles above the Earth.

At certain times of the year, particularly large numbers of shooting stars can be observed—the spectacular

Meteoroids are only visible when they enter the Earth's atmosphere. The friction causes them to glow with heat. Usually they appear faint at first, become brighter, then fade, finally ending in a flash. From the direction and velocity of meteoroids their orbits can be estimated. Sizes can be calculated from the brightness of the flashes.

meteor streams. A 'stream' will occur when the Earth, in its orbit about the Sun, passes through the orbit of an accumulation of meteoroids.

What are the origins of meteoroids? Certainly most of them seem to be a product of the disintegration of those small wanderers of the solar system, the comets.

Meteorites

It is fortunate for the inhabitants of the Earth that meteoroids do, in the main, burn out in the upper reaches of the atmosphere. Otherwise the Earth's surface would be continually bombarded with very rapidly moving particles.

Occasionally, however, larger bodies actually reach the surface still intact; not all the solid material has vaporized. These are the *meteorites*. They range in size from the dimensions of a pebble to great blocks several tons in weight.

The largest known meteorite fell in South Africa during prehistoric times. It weighs 60 tons and must have originally weighed about 80 tons. Another, of 33 tons, has been recovered from Greenland. Probably the most massive body of all reaching the Earth's surface was the meteorite responsible for the Arizona Crater, U.S.A. The crater is three-quarters of a mile in diameter and 600 feet deep.

Usually meteorites fall into one of two classes — the *stones* (or *aerolites*), and the *irons* (or *siderites*). The stones make up about 90% of all known meteorites. They consist largely of silicates and are not very different from the rocks making the crust of the Earth. The irons are metallic bodies, consisting of mostly the element iron (usually about 90%), some nickel

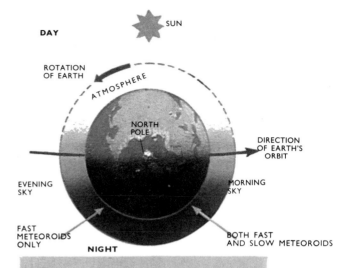

In the evening, only fast meteoroids coming up from behind the Earth will enter the atmosphere. In the morning, the same region will be on the forward side of the Earth and both fast and slow meteoroids will enter. Consequently meteors are always more plentiful in the morning skies.

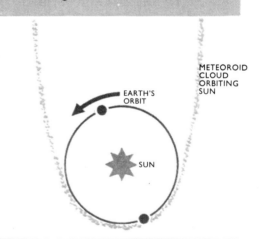

Meteor streams occur when the orbit of the Earth intersects the orbit of a meteoroid cloud.

(usually about 8%) and traces of other elements. A few meteorites — the *siderolites* — are composed of both silicates and iron.

The composition of meteorites, and the fact that they all show signs of a previous molten state, suggest that they may have resulted from the break-up of a larger body, perhaps a former planet of our solar system.

49

CHAPTER FIFTEEN

Comets

A COMET is a collection of lumps of matter. Probably none of the lumps has a diameter greater than 30 miles, and the total mass of the comet is almost certainly less than one ten-thousandth of the mass of the Earth. In size and mass, the comet is insignificant compared with the planets of the Solar System. But as a comet approaches the Sun, its brightness increases enormously. It develops a luminous tail which may be up to 200 million miles long—twice the distance of the Earth from the Sun—and the comet may appear as one of the most prominent objects in the sky.

At one time it was thought that the appearance of a comet was entirely unpredictable. But many comets are regular visitors. They are in fact part of the Solar System: like the planets, they orbit the Sun, but unlike the planets, their orbits are highly elliptical. The Sun is at one of the *foci* of a very elongated ellipse. At one end of its orbit the comet passes close to the

Sun; at the other end, it may travel to the extremity of the Solar System, perhaps ten million million miles away from the Sun (a hundred thousand times the distance of the Earth from the Sun).

At the outermost point of its orbit the comet is totally invisible. It is so small that it cannot reflect enough light from the Sun to be visible, and so cold that it emits no light of its own. The lumps of solid denser matter are coated with gases—including methane (CH_4), carbon monoxide (CO) and cyanogen (C_2N_2)—frozen solid in the intense cold of the outer regions of the Solar System. As it approaches the Sun (and hence the Earth) it reflects more light, and can be detected with a telescope. It intercepts radiation streaming out from the Sun, and this radiation evaporates part of the comet material, directing it away from the Sun, to form the comet tail.

The tail always points away from the Sun. There are two theories which

Two theories of the formation of the comet tail

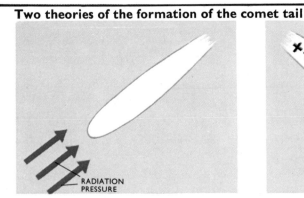

RADIATION PRESSURE

The pressure of the Sun's radiation drives small particles away from the comet head.

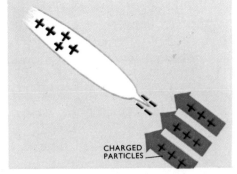

CHARGED PARTICLES

Electrically charged particles from the Sun repel charged particles in the comet.

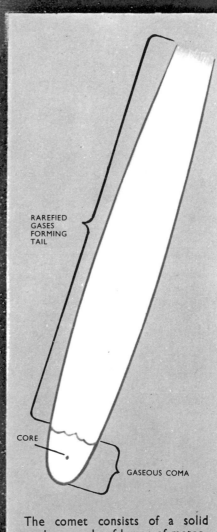

RAREFIED
GASES
FORMING
TAIL

CORE

GASEOUS COMA

The comet consists of a solid nucleus, made of lumps of meteoric rock. This may be about 400 miles across. Surrounding it is the gaseous coma, about 80,000 miles in diameter. The tail may be up to 200,000,000 miles long.

explain why this is so. According to one theory, the tail is forced away from the Sun by the *pressure* of the radiation emitted by the Sun (all kinds of radiation, including heat and light, exert a pressure, called a *radiation pressure*). But one recent comet, the Arend-Roland comet, first seen in 1956, developed an odd 'spike' pointing in the opposite direction, towards the Sun. The spike lasted for only a short time during the end of April, 1957, but it is difficult to account for it on the *radiation pressure* theory.

The comet's tail is probably formed when it is bombarded by electrically charged particles, also emitted by the Sun. Electrostatic forces repel the tail away from the Sun. On this theory, a tail pointing towards the Sun is possible, for charged particles can both repel and attract each other (like charges repel, unlike charges attract). Under certain circumstances, part of the tail might become charged so that it would be attracted towards the Sun.

The comet goes round the Sun, and then starts back on its long journey through the Solar System. Encke's comet will be back again in about 3·3 years. It has the shortest period of any known comet, and, since it was first discovered in 1786, not a single return

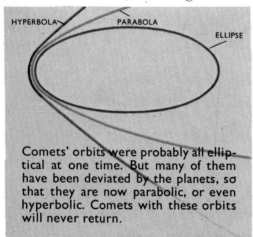

Comets' orbits were probably all elliptical at one time. But many of them have been deviated by the planets, so that they are now parabolic, or even hyperbolic. Comets with these orbits will never return.

has been missed, although the comet can be seen only with the aid of a telescope.

Comets are so small and so comparatively light that they are easily deflected as they pass by the planets, especially the two largest, Jupiter and Saturn. Their paths may be distorted so much that they fly off into space, and never approach the Sun again. Although many comets do come back at fairly regular intervals, the *period* (i.e. the time between consecutive times of closest approach of the Sun) is likely to be affected if the comet's path takes it near Jupiter or Saturn. The most famous of all comets, Halley's comet, has a period of about 76 years. It was last seen in 1910, and it is expected to return in 1986. But some of its appearances have been delayed by up to 15 months because it approached Jupiter and Saturn too closely.

Each time a comet approaches the Sun, it grows a fresh tail. So matter is being continually evaporated from the comet, and it becomes gradually smaller and smaller. Some comets have been seen to disintegrate. Biela's comet split into two parts as it approached the Sun in 1846. The two parts drifted apart, and they were seen as two separate comets when they next approached the Sun in 1852. The comets then broke up into smaller pieces, which were observed during a later orbit as 'shooting stars'.

Comets are being continually lost through disintegration. Still more are lost as they are deflected away into space by the planets. There is no evidence that the Solar System catches comets, but even though it seems to be steadily losing them, about four new comets are discovered each year.

CHAPTER SIXTEEN

Radiation Belts around the Earth

THE EARTH acts like a huge magnet. Using its magnetic field, it waylays some of the electrically charged particles which are continually shooting through space. The particles, because they are electrically charged, are affected by the Earth. Some of them are repelled away into space and others penetrate the Earth's magnetic field, and are caught. Already moved from their original paths, they are forced to travel in tightening spirals around the Earth. Some reach the Earth's surface. Some of them are trapped outside the atmosphere, in the Earth's *radiation belts*.

The origin of the trapped particles is unknown. They are probably *cosmic rays*, particles of high energy blasted away from exploding stars. By the time they approach the Earth, it is virtually impossible to tell where they have come from. Every time the charged particles pass near the magnetic field, their paths are bent, usually into spirals. Negatively charged particles (electrons) spiral in one direction. Positively charged protons spiral in the opposite direction.

Most of the trapped cosmic radiation consists of either protons or electrons. Electrons are very much lighter than protons. Consequently they are more easily trapped, and are forced to spiral around the Earth in the outer radiation belt about 12,000 miles above the Earth's surface. Protons have a bigger mass and can penetrate deeper before they are trapped. Protons go into the inner radiation belt, which is only about 1,000 miles from the Earth.

These two radiation traps, one mainly for protons and one mainly for electrons, are called the *Van Allen Belts*. James A. Van Allen, an Ameri-

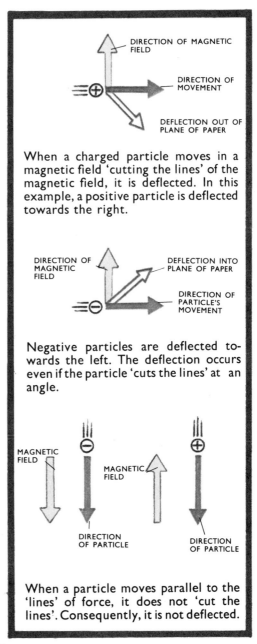

When a charged particle moves in a magnetic field 'cutting the lines' of the magnetic field, it is deflected. In this example, a positive particle is deflected towards the right.

Negative particles are deflected towards the left. The deflection occurs even if the particle 'cuts the lines' at an angle.

When a particle moves parallel to the 'lines' of force, it does not 'cut the lines'. Consequently, it is not deflected.

can physicist, was in charge of the research team which discovered them. The radiation belts were discovered by one of the first artificial satellites in 1958. Geiger counters sent up to record cosmic ray intensities transmitted strange results back to Earth. An unexpectedly high amount of radiation overloaded the counters and jammed them. The satellite, Explorer 1, had encroached into the radiation belts.

Later satellites have carried more adequate counting instruments. They are used to record not only the intensity of the radiation (the number of charged particles hitting the instrument) but also the *magnetic field* extending out into space. Radiation is trapped by magnetic effects, and the radiation belts have been found to follow roughly the contours of the Earth's magnetic field. Between the two Van Allen belts is a no-man's land, where practically no energetic particles can remain for long. Beyond the outer Van Allen belt is a region of less energetic orbiting electrons. Presumably they have not been travelling fast enough to penetrate deeper into the Earth's magnetic field. All the belts occupy a region called the *magnetosphere*.

The Effect of the Solar Wind

The magnetosphere is the region where the Earth's magnetic field is influential. However, the magnetosphere is not a symmetrical sphere. The field around an ordinary bar magnet is symmetrical, and the Earth's magnetic field is thought to be similar to the field around a magnet. But the magnetosphere is distorted by the effect of the Sun.

Streams of particles and other kinds of radiation are emitted by the Sun.

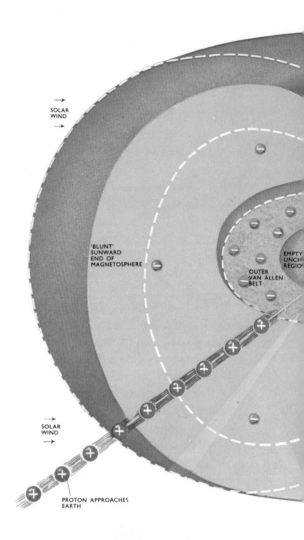

SOLAR WIND →

'BLUNT' SUNWARD END OF MAGNETOSPHERE

OUTER VAN ALLEN BELT

EMPTY UNCH REGIO

SOLAR WIND →

PROTON APPROACHES EARTH

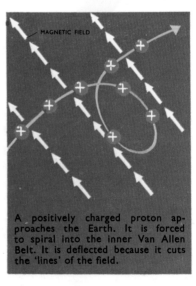

MAGNETIC FIELD

A positively charged proton approaches the Earth. It is forced to spiral into the inner Van Allen Belt. It is deflected because it cuts the 'lines' of the field.

54

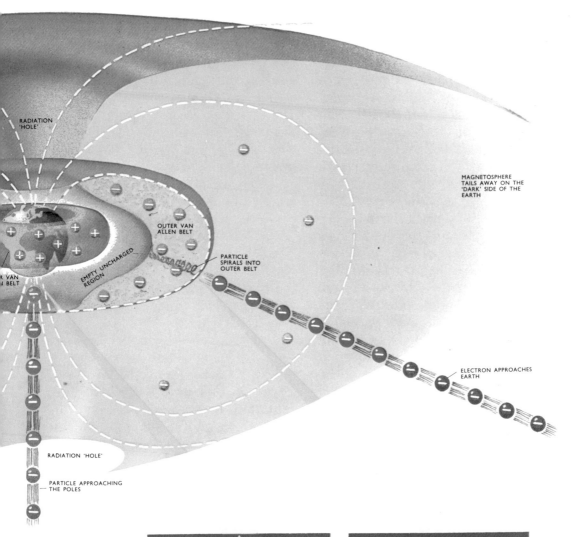

RADIATION 'HOLE'

MAGNETOSPHERE TAILS AWAY ON THE 'DARK' SIDE OF THE EARTH

OUTER VAN ALLEN BELT

EMPTY UNCHARGED REGION

PARTICLE SPIRALS INTO OUTER BELT

ELECTRON APPROACHES EARTH

RADIATION 'HOLE'

PARTICLE APPROACHING THE POLES

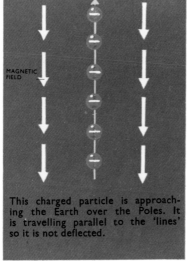

MAGNETIC FIELD

This charged particle is approaching the Earth over the Poles. It is travelling parallel to the 'lines' so it is not deflected.

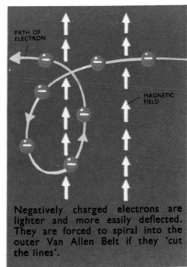

PATH OF ELECTRON

MAGNETIC FIELD

Negatively charged electrons are lighter and more easily deflected. They are forced to spiral into the outer Van Allen Belt if they 'cut the lines'.

More are emitted when the Sun's surface is disturbed by sunspots and solar flares. Particles streaming out from the Sun form a solar 'wind'. Their effect is to blunt the side of the 'sphere' facing the Sun (this side is over the sunlit half of the Earth). On the dark side of the Earth, the magnetosphere is pulled out away from the Earth (and from the Sun).

Radiation Gaps over the Poles

The Earth's radiation trap is incomplete. There are two large holes in it over the polar regions, above latitudes of $70°$ to $75°$ north and south of the Equator. In this region, the Earth's field does not hinder particles coming in from outer space.

They are not trapped because of the peculiar interaction between charged particles and magnetic fields. When the charged particles travel *parallel* to the 'lines' of the magnetic field (as they do when approaching the Poles) they experience no force whatsoever. Their paths are not bent and they do not spiral around. Both electrons and protons can go straight through to the Earth's surface. Hence, there can be no radiation belts above the polar regions.

The Artificial Belts

Not all the energetic particles of the radiation belts are trapped from outer space. Since 1958, new man-made belts of radiation have been put up there. Atomic bombs, exploded in the upper atmosphere, released thousands of millions of millions of millions of millions of high-energy electrons. The object of the experiments was to see how these energetic particles are affected by the Earth's field, how quickly they begin to spiral into radiation belts, and how long the artificial belts can stay there.

On the underside of the inner Van Allen belt, the remains of American 'Starfish' experiments still persist. Nuclear explosions 250 miles above the Earth's surface caused vivid polar aurorae (which are thought to be associated with the radiation belts), and then high-energy electrons, end-products of the nuclear explosion, quickly dispersed into a definite belt. The remnants of a Russian nuclear explosion congregated in the uncharged region between the two Van Allen Belts. However, this radiation quickly disappeared.

A great deal of research remains to be done before the radiation belts are mapped completely. A little of the work is done by balloons—most of it is now done with artificial satellites. The radiation in the belts may be harmful to human beings, so it is important to know its extent, and intensity.

CHAPTER SEVENTEEN

Cosmic Rays

SHOWERS of cosmic rays are continually pouring down on the Earth. We cannot escape them even by going indoors, for cosmic rays are capable of penetrating bricks and mortar. Cosmic rays are the particles of incredibly high energy which come from outside and inside the Solar System.

Although they are called rays, they are not like light rays, or their higher-energy counterparts, X-rays and gamma-rays. For these are all wave-like disturbances — electro-magnetic waves. Cosmic rays, on the other hand, are *particles*. They have energies far in excess of the energies Man can give his artificially-accelerated particles. The proton-synchrotron at Geneva has so far produced particles with energies of over 30 thousand million electron volts. (An electron-volt is the energy acquired by an electron when it is accelerated through a voltage difference of one volt). But the energies of cosmic rays have been estimated at between ten million and a million-million-million electron volts — i.e. up to a hundred million times more energetic than the particles Man can produce.

In most of his experiments with the particles produced in machines like the proton synchrotron, Man is trying to find more and more minute details about the structure of the nuclei of atoms. If he can produce very energetic particles, he can penetrate deeper into the nucleus, and so get better information. Obviously, he can penetrate deeper with cosmic rays donated free of charge by unknown sources in the Universe than he can

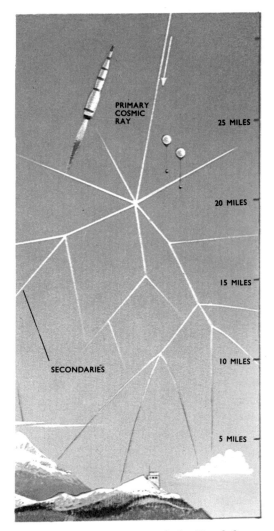

Primary cosmic rays reach the Earth from outer space, and collide with atoms in the atmosphere. Rays and particles showering from these collisions are called *secondary* cosmic rays.

with particles produced by highly-expensive machines. This is the main reason for the great interest in cosmic rays. Many important discoveries in nuclear physics have been made using them.

Cosmic rays were originally discovered in the early twentieth century, when scientists were experimenting with X-rays, radio-activity and electrical discharges through gases. One of the measuring instruments they were using was the gold-leaf electroscope, two thin leaves of gold which, when given an electric charge, repelled each other and diverged. The amount they diverged depended on the amount of charge they had received. The gold-leaf electroscope was usually insulated, so that the charge on its leaves could not leak away. But if it were placed in the path of X-rays, or rays from a lump of radioactive material, the two leaves of the electroscope rapidly flopped together. They did this because the radiation had ionized the air around the electroscope, separating positive charges from negative charges, and allowed the air to conduct the charge away from the leaves.

When there were no radiations around, the air behaved like a fairly good electrical insulator. But it was not a perfect insulator, for the leaves very gradually lost their charge, and fell together. No matter how they tried to insulate the plates, they would always fall together over a period of time.

Scientists argued that there must be some other kind of radiation around. In about 1910 they started to look for another source of radiation, testing whether it originated from outside the atmosphere by sending gold-leaf electroscopes into the atmosphere with balloons. By 1912 they had found out that the intensity of the radiation increased with height—the gold leaves fell together more quickly at higher altitudes. This meant that the radiations must come from outside the atmosphere, and because of this they were given the name *cosmic rays*.

Cosmic rays are thought to be particles ejected in supernovae explosions, like that of the Crab nebula. But the rays are deviated so much by magnetic fields in space that it is almost impossible to tell where they come from.

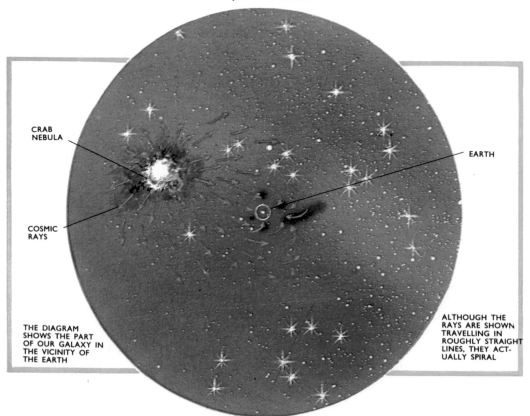

CRAB NEBULA

EARTH

COSMIC RAYS

THE DIAGRAM SHOWS THE PART OF OUR GALAXY IN THE VICINITY OF THE EARTH

ALTHOUGH THE RAYS ARE SHOWN TRAVELLING IN ROUGHLY STRAIGHT LINES, THEY ACTUALLY SPIRAL

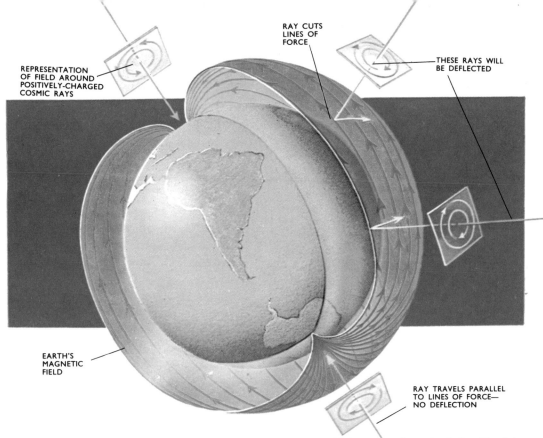

RAY CUTS
LINES OF
FORCE

REPRESENTATION
OF FIELD AROUND
POSITIVELY-CHARGED
COSMIC RAYS

THESE RAYS WILL
BE DEFLECTED

EARTH'S
MAGNETIC
FIELD

RAY TRAVELS PARALLEL
TO LINES OF FORCE—
NO DEFLECTION

Rays coming in towards the Poles are travelling parallel to the 'lines' of the Earth's magnetic field of force. They are not deflected. The rays approaching the Equator 'cut across the lines'. Whenever they do this, a force acts on them, and they are deflected away. So more cosmic rays reach the Poles than the Equator.

Later balloon experiments showed that this radiation increased in intensity up to 15 miles high, then steadily decreased between heights of 15 and 25 miles. After that the radiation stayed constant with altitude. Other experiments demonstrated the great penetrating power of cosmic rays. Even when it was protected by a lead shielding, the electroscope lost its charge.

The Nature of Cosmic Rays

These experiments established the fact that radiation was reaching the Earth from outer space. What kind of radiation was it? Radiation could consist of either waves, like gamma-rays, or particles, like protons and electrons. It was first thought that cosmic rays were very, very energetic gamma-rays, but this was disproved by other experiments. For the main difference between waves and particles is that particles can carry electric charges—waves cannot. If any evidence could be found that the rays carried electrical charges, then obviously they must be particles.

Then it was noticed that the intensity of the cosmic radiation at sea level varied with latitude. Rays reaching the Earth were about ten per cent more intense near the Poles than near the Equator. The interpretation of this was that the rays nearer the Equator were being deflected away by the Earth's magnetic field. As they could be deflected by a magnetic field, the rays must be capable of behaving like magnets, i.e. they must be moving charged particles. From the way they were deflected, it was worked out that they must be positively charged. The cosmic ray intensity varies very little from day to night, so it is known that only a very small proportion can come from the Sun. The vast majority originate from some source outside the Solar System.

There are two kinds of cosmic rays, *primary* rays and *secondary rays*. The primary rays are the original rays coming from outer space and striking the top of the Earth's atmosphere. The secondaries are the rays produced by the collision of primaries with the atoms in the atmosphere. The bulk of the rays reaching the Earth's surface are secondaries.

Primary Rays

Primary rays usually penetrate only about 10 miles through the atmosphere before being converted into secondaries. Primaries are made up of 86% hydrogen nuclei (protons) and 13% helium nuclei (alpha particles). The remaining 1% consists of nuclei of heavier elements, such as lithium, carbon, calcium and iron. Most of them are travelling at almost the speed of light.

They arrive at the outside of the atmosphere with very great energies. So if they happen to collide with atoms in the atmosphere, the collision is usually very violent. They can penetrate deep into the nuclei of the atoms, and completely disintegrate them. Very energetic particles may be ejected and several new particles have been discovered among the remnants of these collisions.

One of these is the *positron*, the positively charged counterpart of the electron. One of the energetic interactions in the atmosphere produced a powerful gamma-ray. The gamma-ray then turned into two particles, an electron and a positron. These two particles are identical in mass and size, and the only difference between them is that one is negatively charged and the other is positively charged. Two bits of matter had apparently been created out of nothing. But they had been made from the *energy* of the gamma-ray, and it is possible to create particles out of a large amount of energy just as it is to do what the nuclear reactor does — convert a small amount of matter into a large amount of energy.

Often the collisions involve many particles, and are very complicated. One of the most successful ways of finding out what is happening is to send stacks of photographic plates, via balloon, into the upper atmosphere. Special *nuclear emulsion* is used on the plates, and the passage of the particles is recorded as they blacken atoms in the emulsion.

Secondary Rays

Very few of the primary rays reach the Earth's surface. They have nearly all collided with particles in the atmosphere, to produce the secondary cosmic rays.

Secondaries are a motley assortment of particles, resulting from an infinite variety of interactions. These consist of particles like the *hyperons* and the *mesons,* as well as electrons, positrons and neutrons. Associated with them are high energy gamma-rays and X-rays. One primary can produce a cascade of secondaries whose paths zig-zag like forked lightning to Earth.

CHAPTER EIGHTEEN

The Birth and Death of a Star

THE SUN is an ordinary sort of star. It is of smallish size, of average brightness, and in its middle age. Although the Sun appears to alter little from day to day, from year to year, or even from century to century, it is in fact slowly evolving and changing with time.

The Sun was 'born' a few thousand million years ago. It will probably 'die' in a few thousand million years' time.

Birth

Stars start their lives as huge clouds of gas, practically all of it

Stars are still being 'born' in the dense dark clouds of gas and dust obscuring part of the Orion Nebula. The new star cannot be seen until it radiates enough heat and light to penetrate the dark clouds.

The star has become a *nova* and is nearing the end of its active life. The 'fronds' are the outer layers of the star, which are being ejected into space. This nova is in the constellation of Perseus.

hydrogen. The gas is very, very rarefied, the diameter of the cloud being initially about one light year (5,880,000,000,000 miles). Gravitational forces acting between the atoms bring them closer together and the huge hydrogen cloud, the *protostar*, gradually starts to contract. The life of the star has begun.

When atoms are very far apart, they have what is called *gravitational* energy. This is a kind of *potential energy,* and it disappears as the atoms are pulled closer together. No energy can be completely lost. It must be converted into energy of another kind —in this instance into giving the atoms extra kinetic energy, making them move faster. Temperature in the rarefied gases of the protostar simply depends on the speed of the molecules. In the beginning they are mov-

A huge, rarefied cloud of hydrogen gas, the protostar, condenses to form the star. Gravitational forces acting between the hydrogen atoms pull them closer together.

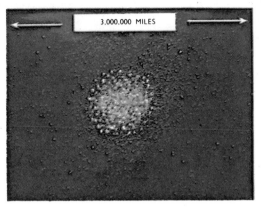

The contraction stops when the star gets so hot that the gravitational contraction is balanced by its tendency to expand with heating.

ing so fast that their energy is equivalent to a temperature of 10,000° C. The heating effect is, however, small, because it is confined to the atoms and there is none in the large spaces between atoms.

As the hydrogen atoms are pulled together, their kinetic energy increases. They become hotter, move faster, and start to collide with other atoms.

The protostar which became the Sun contracted to a far denser cloud of hydrogen, now a sphere only about 800,000 miles in diameter. By then it was about 70 million years old. It had probably already given birth to the planets, formed from parts of the gas cloud.

The atoms in the core of a newly contracted star are so energetic that their temperature approaches a million degrees Centigrade. The star now settles down to a steady, far slower process of evolution, which will take up 90% of its active life, and see it through youth to old age. Gradually, the hydrogen atoms are built up into heavier elements in *thermonuclear* reactions.

Middle Age

The nucleus of the hydrogen atom, the proton, is the main building block from which the nuclei of atoms of all elements can be made. At the enormously high temperature in the star's core the hydrogen gas is *ionized*, i.e. protons are separated from electrons. A few protons hit each other sufficiently hard to join to each other, emitting a positive electron and becoming heavy hydrogen, or *deuterium* (one proton, one neutron). In nuclear processes, a proton can change into a neutron by emitting a positive electron (a positron).

Another proton joins on, to form the light isotope of helium (two protons, one neutron). More reactions follow, and very, very slowly, the whole process probably taking hundreds of millions of years, a stock of the heavier helium isotope (two protons, two neutrons) is built up in the core of the star.

63

The temperature inside the core of the star is now about a million degrees. Thermonuclear reactions start, hydrogen being gradually converted into helium.

The helium core expands. The star expands very slowly, as it becomes hotter. The Sun is midway between this stage and the previous one.

Thermonuclear reactions are enormous sources of energy, since a large amount of energy is released when light elements combine. The Sun is already about half-way through this stage of its life and has been radiating vast quantities of energy for a few thousand million years. Yet it has used only a small fraction of its hydrogen 'fuel' to produce this energy.

Most of the star's energy is radiated out into space. However, a little is retained, and this means that the star becomes hotter, and the temperature within its core rises to 100,000,000°C. When this temperature is reached, roughly 10% of its hydrogen has been converted into helium, practically all of it contained in the inner core. The part of the star where the hydrogen is 'burnt' to form helium is confined to a thin layer, or 'skin', around the core. The core increases in size as the hydrogen-burning layer spreads out, and the star as a whole slowly expands.

Death
Events start to move more quickly.

Now the helium atoms start to join together to form heavier and heavier elements. These reactions all release vast amounts of thermonuclear energy. The star gets rapidly hotter, and expands far more quickly.

In some stars, the thermonuclear reactions get out of control. Heavier elements are quickly built up until iron, atomic weight 56, is produced. Iron and helium are the two most stable elements and all matter prefers to exist in these stable forms. The star has been building up stable iron from stable helium. But now, under certain conditions, the reverse process takes place. To disintegrate iron into helium, a vast amount of energy is needed, and *quickly*. The only quickly available energy source is the gravitational energy which the star has been gradually building up as a result of its expansion. To release this energy, the star must contract. To supply the reactions with energy, the contraction leads to a rapid inward collapse of the star.

A collapsing star is violently un-

64

Helium atoms start to combine to form heavier elements. The temperature rises rapidly, and the star expands into a *red giant.*

The giant becomes a *nova,* ejecting half its matter into space. All the 'fuel' is used up, and the star contracts into a *white dwarf (below).*

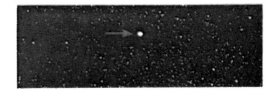

stable. It gains too much gravitational energy too quickly. The collapse is halted as the star explodes, ejecting most of its matter into space, in a *supernova.*

Supernovae are, however, very rare occurrences. Most stars manage to avoid going through this stage. They build up a concentration of heavier elements, expand, become *red giants,* and start to lose a lot of their outer layer of gas into space. The star becomes a *nova,* as it ejects half of its matter, and appears far brighter. The star has already burnt up most of its fuel. What happens to it now is not exactly known. It is most likely that the star contracts again, this time to conserve its heat. Its final contraction turns it into a dense *white dwarf.*

White dwarfs are so small that their radii are comparable with those of the larger planets of the Solar System. The huge mass of the star is condensed into a relatively tiny volume. Because of this, its density is far higher than the density of any substance known on Earth. At the centre of a white dwarf, a single matchboxful of matter has a mass of several tons.

It is now roughly 5,000,000,000 years old. With no more fuel to burn, the star gradually cools, and 'dies' as it grows fainter and fainter, finally becoming too faint to be seen.

Gas condenses to form a star. Gravitational forces pull the gas into the centre. The star becomes hot and thermonuclear reactions start inside its core. The star continues like this for a few thousand million years, slowly expanding.

GRAVITATIONAL FORCES

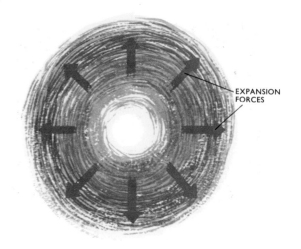

EXPANSION FORCES

CHAPTER NINETEEN

Pulsating Stars

POLARIS, the Pole star, changes almost imperceptibly in brightness every four days. Regularly it brightens and then fades again. Polaris is a *pulsating* star, of the kind called *Cepheid (see-feed) variables*. Cepheids are bright, yellow, luminous stars. But Cepheids are distinguishable from all other types of pulsating

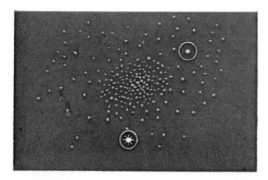

Cepheid variables are discovered from photographs like these. The two photographs of the same cluster of stars (taken on different days) show that two are pulsating.

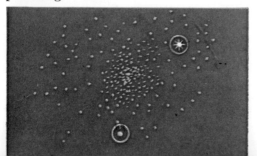

stars because the time between one brightness peak and the next (the *period*) seems to depend on the brightness, or *luminosity* of the star.

Luminous pulsating stars have long periods and less luminous stars have shorter periods. The periods range from just over a day (for less luminous stars) to a few weeks for the most luminous Cepheid variable. Starting with the facts about period and luminosity, astronomers can work out, in a round-about fashion, the distance of the star from the Earth.

The brightness of the star, as seen from the Earth, is called the *apparent magnitude*. (Magnitude in Astronomy does not mean the *size* of the star). The apparent magnitude is not, however, the true brightness of the star. A nearby, dim star can have just the same apparent magnitude as a brighter, more distant star. The light has travelled a longer distance, and a smaller proportion of it is intercepted by the Earth. Theoretically, at twice the distance, the apparent brightness is only a quarter. At three times the

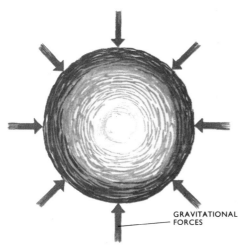

GRAVITATIONAL
FORCES

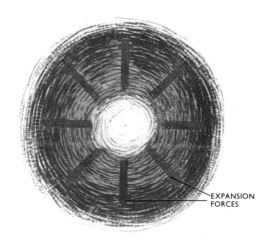

EXPANSION
FORCES

Gravitational forces and expansion forces are unbalanced, so the star pulsates. On the left, the expansion forces are greater than the gravitational forces, and the star expands. Above, the star contracts. Right, it expands again, and so on.

distance, it is down to a ninth. The apparent brightness decreases as the *square of the distance apart* increases. Other factors may dim the light, but this law (called the Inverse Square Law) is the basis for estimating the true brightness or luminosity of the star.

The distances of the nearest Cepheid variables are found by a geometrical method, the *method of parallax*. Their brightness is also measured, and then their luminosities can be found. Their periods are also found. All the results are plotted as points on a graph with luminosity along one axis and period along the other. It is discovered that the points lie roughly along a straight line.

When a new Cepheid variable is discovered, and it is too far away for its distance to be measured in any other way, the straight-line graph is used. Two things are known—the *period*, and the fact that the 'point' for this star must lie roughly on the straight line. If a star in our own

Galaxy has a period of four days, it must have a luminosity about 600 times greater than the Sun for the 'point' to lie on the straight line. The luminosity found from the graph is compared with the apparent brightness, and the distance of the star can be worked out.

Of the 15,000 observable, named and listed stars, about 3% are Cepheid variables. The Cepheids in our galaxy (the Milky Way) lie mostly within the main disc of the Galaxy. A few older Cepheids lie outside the disc, in the region known as the *halo*. The Cepheids in the disc of the Galaxy are fairly young stars, but it is thought that they must be in a later stage of their development than the Sun. The Sun is not a pulsating star, but it could become one eventually.

The Life of a Cepheid

When a star is first 'born', a huge volume of hydrogen gas and dust contracts inwards, attracted towards its own centre by gravitational forces. The atoms inside its core become hot and densely packed, and thermonuclear reactions begin. Atoms start to join together, and the star behaves like a vast thermonuclear reactor. The star grows hotter as more of the hydrogen 'fuel' is 'burnt', and the tendency

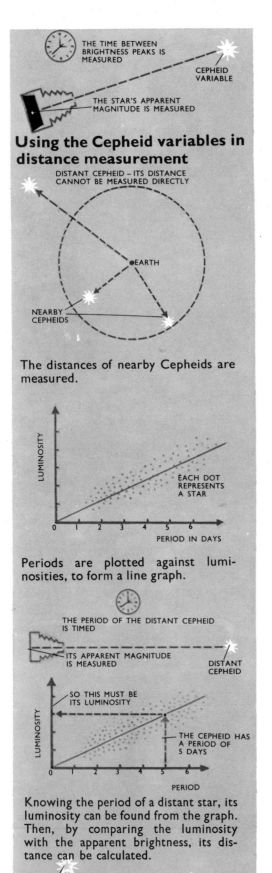

Using the Cepheid variables in distance measurement

THE TIME BETWEEN BRIGHTNESS PEAKS IS MEASURED

CEPHEID VARIABLE

THE STAR'S APPARENT MAGNITUDE IS MEASURED

DISTANT CEPHEID – ITS DISTANCE CANNOT BE MEASURED DIRECTLY

EARTH

NEARBY CEPHEIDS

The distances of nearby Cepheids are measured.

LUMINOSITY

EACH DOT REPRESENTS A STAR

PERIOD IN DAYS

Periods are plotted against luminosities, to form a line graph.

THE PERIOD OF THE DISTANT CEPHEID IS TIMED

ITS APPARENT MAGNITUDE IS MEASURED

DISTANT CEPHEID

SO THIS MUST BE ITS LUMINOSITY

LUMINOSITY

THE CEPHEID HAS A PERIOD OF 5 DAYS

PERIOD

Knowing the period of a distant star, its luminosity can be found from the graph. Then, by comparing the luminosity with the apparent brightness, its distance can be calculated.

DISTANT STAR

NEARBY STAR

is for the star to expand. But the inward gravitational forces, which are still acting, prevent this.

In stable stars, like the Sun, outwards and inwards forces just about balance each other, so the size and brightness of the Sun does not alter very much. However, in a Cepheid variable, the forces have probably become unbalanced. The star has used up a great deal of its hydrogen 'fuel' and it is starting to use its supply of the gas helium (formed from the hydrogen) in building up heavier and heavier elements. Enormous amounts of heat are released during the reactions. The star suddenly expands, but the reactions are not supplying enough heat to keep the expansion going. Gravitational forces gain the upper hand, and the star contracts. The star oscillates in and out, appearing alternately brighter and fainter.

Once the oscillations have started, it is difficult for them to stop. However, periods of Cepheids have been observed to lengthen gradually with time, possibly because the oscillations are dying down. It has been estimated that the star continues to pulsate for a few thousand years. During this time the star as a whole has expanded considerably, become more luminous, and has probably developed into a *red giant* or huge red star. While its period is lengthening, the star is growing more luminous, in accordance with the period/luminosity law.

This theory explains some of the observed facts about some of the Cepheid variables, but it does not explain all of them. Some Cepheid variables are known to be much older stars, at a different stage in their development. They are unlikely to be going through their expansion stage now.

CHAPTER TWENTY

Supernovae

THE CHEMICAL composition of stars, such as the Sun, can be found by examining their light with a spectroscope. When the Sun's light is split into its spectrum with a simple prism, it appears to be an unbroken band of all colours of the rainbow. Closer examination with a spectroscope reveals that it is crossed by dark lines, *Fraunhofer lines,* marking the wavelengths of light which have been absorbed by atoms in the outer, cooler layers of the Sun's chromosphere. Certain elements absorb certain wavelengths; so it is possible to identify the elements present in the light-emitting chromosphere.

In the Sun, only one atom in 50,000 is of the element iron. But the presence of even this minute amount is difficult to explain. Most of it is thought to be a legacy from *supernovae* (stellar explosions) in an older generation of stars and galaxies. They started out with only hydrogen as a building block. Gradually, as a result of thermonuclear reactions, heavier and heavier elements were built up. In some of the more massive stars the reactions got out of hand, and iron, a very stable element, could be formed. Then, suddenly, conditions favoured the break-up of iron nuclei into the next most stable element, helium. A vast amount of energy is required to break up iron. The star undergoes a collapse to provide the energy from its stockpile of gravitational potential energy. It becomes violently unstable, and explodes as helium is reconverted to iron.

Up to 90% of the star's mass is flung out into space, to form part of the material for the next generation of stars (such as our own Sun) which have thus built up their present stock of heavier elements without starting from scratch with hydrogen.

Two stable elements, helium and iron, play an important part in supernovae.

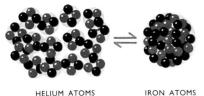

HELIUM ATOMS   IRON ATOMS

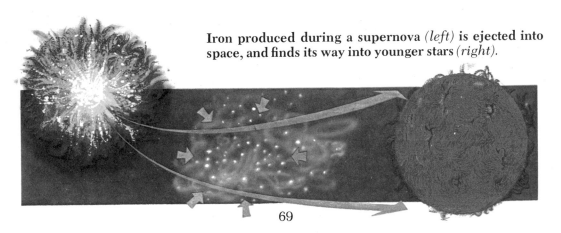

Iron produced during a supernova *(left)* **is ejected into space, and finds its way into younger stars** *(right).*

CHAPTER TWENTY-ONE

Families of Stars

IT HAS BEEN estimated that there are 100,000,000,000,000,000,000 stars in the Universe. They can be divided roughly into two families, or *populations*. *Population II* is the old-established family of stars, while *Population I* stars are relative new-comers. Members of the older family live longer and, although some of them have long-since 'died', there are still millions of millions of survivors.

What is more surprising is that the stars of the two families can be arranged in 'family trees'. Subdivisions within the family appear as branches away from the main stem of the 'family tree'. This method of arrangement is known as a *Hertzsprung-Russell diagram*, after two astronomers, Ejnar Hertzsprung, a Dane who worked at Leiden Observatory, and Henry N. Russell, an American who was the director of the Princeton Observatory. Hertzsprung and Russell invented the 'family tree' arrangement independently.

They were trying to find some order among the many different kinds of stars. There were white stars, yellow stars, red stars, blue stars and even green stars. Was colour a good method of classifying stars? The brightest stars were a thousand million times brighter than the dullest stars. Was brightness a better method of classification?

One important clue is that colour and brightness are related. To show the relationship, the colour of a star is plotted against its brightness on a graph. Colour goes along the horizontal axis, blue stars on the left, ranging through all the colours of the rainbow to red stars on the right. Brightness goes up the vertical axis of the graph. (This is the real, or *absolute* brightness of the star, with its distance away from the Earth taken into account.)

Each star has a certain colour and a certain brightness. This colour and brightness correspond to a single point on the graph. A dim red star is at the lower right-hand corner of the graph. Bright blue stars are at the upper left-

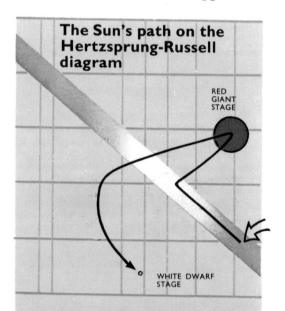

The Sun's path on the Hertzsprung-Russell diagram

RED GIANT STAGE

WHITE DWARF STAGE

The Sun is about 5,000 million years old. 5,000 million years ago, it contracted into a smallish red star. In another 5,000 million years' time, the Sun will have worked its way up the main sequence. It will branch off, expand, and then cross the main sequence again to become a white dwarf.

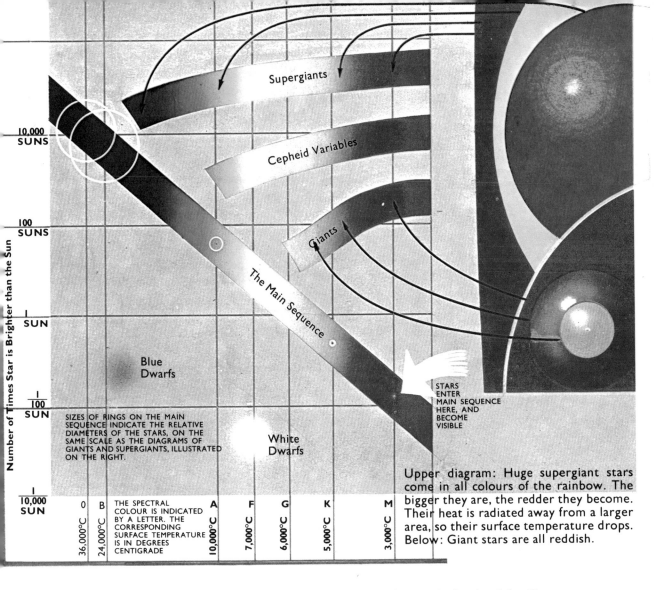

The diagram contains the following labels:

Vertical axis: Number of Times Star is Brighter than the Sun

10,000 SUNS — 100 SUNS — 1 SUN — 1/100 SUN — 1/10,000 SUN

Supergiants

Cepheid Variables

Giants

The Main Sequence

Blue Dwarfs

White Dwarfs

SIZES OF RINGS ON THE MAIN SEQUENCE INDICATE THE RELATIVE DIAMETERS OF THE STARS, ON THE SAME SCALE AS THE DIAGRAMS OF GIANTS AND SUPERGIANTS, ILLUSTRATED ON THE RIGHT.

STARS ENTER MAIN SEQUENCE HERE, AND BECOME VISIBLE

0	B	THE SPECTRAL COLOUR IS INDICATED BY A LETTER. THE CORRESPONDING SURFACE TEMPERATURE IS IN DEGREES CENTIGRADE	A	F	G	K	M
36,000°C	24,000°C		10,000°C	7,000°C	6,000°C	5,000°C	3,000°C

Upper diagram: Huge supergiant stars come in all colours of the rainbow. The bigger they are, the redder they become. Their heat is radiated away from a larger area, so their surface temperature drops. Below: Giant stars are all reddish.

Luminosity brightness, plotted logarithmically, goes up the vertical axis of the Hertz-sprung-Russell diagram. The scale on the horizontal axis represents the colour of the star. This is also a measure of the star's surface temperature.

hand corner. When all the stars of the younger family are plotted in this way, it is found that 90% of them lie on an almost-straight line from the lower right-hand edge to the upper left-hand edge. This line is called the *main sequence*.

Most of the remaining 10% fall into one of two branches, one halfway up the main sequence, and the other near the topmost end of it. The lower branch represents the giant stars, and the upper branch the supergiant stars.

Practically all Population I stars fit on to a well-defined Population I family tree, and there is a similarly well-defined 'tree' for Population II stars. But the two family trees differ. There are fewer stars on the main sequence of older stars, and parts of the main sequence are missing entirely. Most older stars are instead concentrated in the branches away from the main sequence. They break away from the main sequence at an earlier point than do younger stars.

71

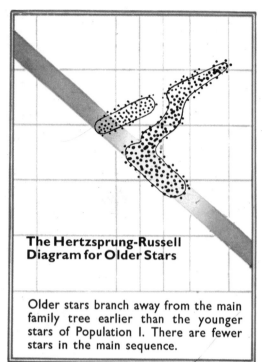

The Hertzsprung-Russell Diagram for Older Stars

Older stars branch away from the main family tree earlier than the younger stars of Population I. There are fewer stars in the main sequence.

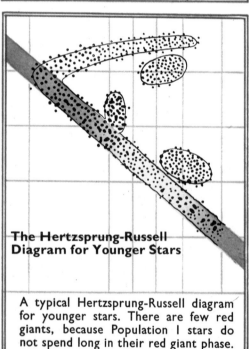

The Hertzsprung-Russell Diagram for Younger Stars

A typical Hertzsprung-Russell diagram for younger stars. There are few red giants, because Population I stars do not spend long in their red giant phase.

Interpreting the Diagram

All stars began in the same way, starting off with similar amounts of material—hydrogen gas, with perhaps heavier elements and interstellar dust—in the form of a huge contracting cloud. Gradually, as the cloud contracted, the star condensed. But stars started to form at different times, developed at different rates, and some became unstable and developed abnormally. Because of this the stars now differ markedly in size, brightness and colour. It is also the reason why they are now strung out along the main sequence and branches of the Hertzsprung-Russell diagram.

Stable stars gradually evolve up the main sequence, becoming brighter and hotter. The colour of the light radiated depends on the temperature. Blue stars are the hottest. And as the star's temperature increases, it gradually expands.

The expansion of the abnormal giant stars takes them into the first branch away from the main sequence. It has taken place so quickly that the stars have cooled, and become redder; expanded, and so become more luminous.

The supergiant stars in the upper branch must be even bigger than the giant stars, for they are 1,000 times brighter. Again, the biggest of them are also the reddest.

One major group of stars has a separate branch between the giant and supergiant branches. These are the unstable *Cepheid* variable stars.

All stars must eventually burn themselves out, and 'die'. They collapse to a tiny dim white star—a white dwarf. These stars are to be found in a group at the bottom of the Hertzsprung-Russell diagram.

CHAPTER TWENTY-TWO

The Milky Way

ON A DARK NIGHT, a faint band of light can be seen stretching across the sky. Its appearance to the naked eye is the reason for its name — the Milky Way. When observed through even a pair of binoculars, the 'milkiness' disappears, and the faint light can be seen to come from myriads of stars, clustered closely together.

The Milky Way is in fact a *galaxy,* a conglomeration of stars, gas and dust 100,000 light years across (a light year is the distance light travels in one year, and is about 5,880,000,000,000 miles). The Sun belongs to this galaxy, and is situated in an insignificant position about 30,000 light years from its centre. In the Universe there are many other galaxies similar to the Milky Way.

The Milky Way can be divided into three main parts. The centre is a spherical bulge of closely-packed stars. Radiating out from it are wispy spiral arms of stars, gas and dust, which form a disc 100,000 light years in diameter and 2,500 light years thick. The third part of the galaxy is its *halo,* a more sparsely populated sphere of stars which is an extension of the closely-packed central 'bulge'. It, too, has a diameter of 100,000 light years.

A diagrammatic end-on view of the Milky Way, as seen from the Earth.

LIMIT OF HALO

CENTRAL BULGE OF OLDER STARS

OBSERVER ON EARTH SEES VIEW FROM DISC

The Earth gets an end-on view of the disc of the Milky Way, since it is itself a part of the disc. This explains why the Milky Way appears as a long thin band, its brightest portion being in the direction of the centre of the galaxy.

Stars in the disc of the Milky Way are slowly rotating about its centre. Stars at the extreme edge take longer to complete one revolution than do those nearer the middle, so they tend to trail behind, and form the spirals. The Sun's orbit around the centre of the Milky Way takes 220,000 million years.

It has been estimated that the Milky Way contains some 200,000 million stars. They are of many different types, at various stages in their evolution, and grouped together in all manner of ways. There is, however, a marked difference between the kind of star that populates the halo and the central core of the galaxy, and the kind of stars that populate the disc. The stars of the halo and centre are found to be much older than the stars of the disc. Astronomers call the older stars *Population II* and the younger

The spiral arms of the Galaxy have been mapped with the aid of Radio Astronomy. Loose, invisible hydrogen gas in the arms can be traced because it emits radio waves.

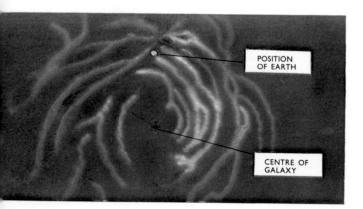

POSITION OF EARTH

CENTRE OF GALAXY

stars *Population I*. The two distinct *Populations* are very important, for they provide clues about the way the galaxy was formed.

The Milky Way probably started its life as an immense spherical cloud of hydrogen gas, that contracted as gravitational forces acting between its gas particles pulled them in towards the centre. The gas was by no means uniformly distributed, and so individual stars formed from denser patches of the contracting gas. More stars tended to form near the centre as this was where the gas was densest. These stars were the first to form in the galaxy, so, according to this theory, we would expect to find all the oldest *Population II* stars in the halo and the centre. And, in fact, *Population II* stars are found to predominate there.

The disc of the Milky Way contains about 500 million stars—only a tiny fraction of the total in the whole galaxy. It was formed as a direct result of the contraction of the rest of the galaxy.

It is likely that the gas cloud was originally rotating slowly about its own centre, and the rotation complicated the contraction. A skater experiences the same kind of phenomenon when he spins. He learns to start the spin with his arms outstretched, and finds he can spin much faster simply by pulling his arms in towards his body. The physical principle which causes this is known as *Conservation of Angular Momentum*, and it applies just as much to the contracting, rotating galaxy as it does to the spinning skater pulling his arms inwards.

The skater would probably be able to control his spin. But the galaxy is unable to hold on to quickly rotating

The Milky Way, originally a huge spherical cloud of whirling hydrogen gas, contracted into a flat, whirling disc with a dense bulge at its centre

gas. What it does is to compromise. The inwards forces and the rotational forces combine to pack some of the matter into a disc. The rearrangement means that the galaxy still has its 'arms outstretched'. By concentrating some of its matter into a rotating disc, the galaxy has compensated for the contraction-towards-the-centre of the rest of the stars.

From this it follows that the disc should be populated by younger stars, of *Population I*, 'born' long after the *Population II* stars were formed. Stars of the older *Population II* developed, aged, ejected some of their matter into space, or even exploded. Dust and gas from older stars would accumulate in the disc. *Population I* stars were formed (and are still being formed) from this matter and from the tenuous clouds of hydrogen which had not already condensed into stars.

The dust in the Milky Way is a nuisance to astronomers, for it obscures the stars beyond it. The 18th century astronomer, William Herschel, saw a very dark patch in the bright Milky Way. He believed that this was a kind of window through which it would be possible to peer into space beyond the Milky Way. But the dark patch had the opposite

effect. It is called a *dark nebula,* and fine particles of dust in it block light. Dark nebulae also contain hydrogen gas, although this does not add very much to the obscuring effect.

When the dark matter takes the form of a globule, about a light year in diameter, it is very likely that a new star is in the process of being 'born' from it. New stars are continually being born in the disc of the Milky Way.

Mapping the Milky Way

Dust is only one of the problems confronting astronomers. Before they can build up a picture of the struc-

The Earth's circumference is about 25,000 miles. The distance of the Sun is about 93,000,000 miles, or 3,720 times the circumference of the Earth.

One light year is over 60,000 times the distance of the Earth from the Sun, i.e. equivalent to 230 million times the Earth's circumference.

The galaxy is about 100,000 light years across, so a journey across it would be equivalent to going 23 million million times around the Earth.

75

ture of the galaxy, they must, of course, know the distance of the stars from the Earth. One way of doing this is called the *parallax* method. The position of the star in the sky is very carefully measured. Then it is measured again when the Earth is at the opposite side of its orbit round the Sun. The Earth's movement causes an apparent change in the position of the star, and the amount of change depends on its distance from the Earth.

The parallax method works for stars which are within 150 light years of the Earth. Stars outside this limit are so far away that their apparent shift of position is too small to be measured. A fraction of the Milky Way could therefore be charted accurately by this method. However, these measurements give no indication of the size of the whole galaxy. Astronomers on Earth are at a disadvantage because all they can see is the end-on view of a disc. Mapping the disc of the galaxy would be simpler if the Earth were in the halo. It also follows that it is easier to map the halo, because the Earth is in the disc. The size of the galaxy has, in fact, been found by measuring the size of the halo.

Many of the halo stars appear faint, because they are very far away. But some of the stars are grouped into *globular clusters*. As their name suggests, these are spherical in shape (the typical shape of the older, *Population II* star-clusters), and they may consist of 100,000 to 1,000,000 stars. About 100 globular clusters are known in the halo of the Milky Way, and they are easily visible. Almost all of them are to be found in one part of the sky. This reinforces the view that the Sun is not in the centre of the Milky Way; otherwise the globular clusters should be evenly distributed over all parts of the sky.

Some stars in the globular clusters appear alternately brighter and fainter with astonishing regularity. They are called *Cepheid variables,* and it has been found that the length of time between peaks of brightness and dimness depends on the brightness of the star. The apparent brightness observed on Earth is, of course, much smaller than the actual brightness, because the light has travelled a long distance from the star before it reaches the Earth. But by knowing the apparent brightness, and calculating the actual brightness, astronomers can calculate the distance of the star from the Earth. This gives the approximate distance of the whole globular cluster. The size of the halo and disc have been found by measuring the distance of all the globular clusters.

The Spiral Arms

Many of the other galaxies in the Universe are *spiral* galaxies. The spiral structure of the Great Nebula in Andromeda, for instance, can be seen clearly (with a telescope) because, from the Earth, we are looking down on to its disc. Spiral 'arms' are a common feature of galaxies, and it is reasonable to suppose that the Milky Way has them too.

The spiral arms are marked by clouds of invisible hydrogen gas. However, although it does not emit visible light, the hydrogen gas does emit *radio waves.* Radio telescopes can pick up radio signals from the gas, and it is possible to plot the position of the gas, and work out how quickly it is moving. The arms do indeed spiral about the centre of the galaxy.

CHAPTER TWENTY-THREE

Stars and Galaxies

A GALAXY is a collection of stars, dust and unattached hydrogen atoms. Average galaxies consist of about ten thousand million stars. So naturally there are a great many more individual stars than galaxies in the universe. However, when photographs of the sky are studied in detail, there appear to be far more galaxies than stars. The reason for this is that individual stars forming a galaxy are widely spaced in relation to their size, while whole galaxies are packed comparatively close together.

The average star is about four light years distant from its nearest neighbour in space—about *ten million times* the star's diameter. The average spacing between galaxies is only about *a hundred times* the galaxy's diameter. Most galaxies are even closer than this to their neighbouring galaxies, because they tend to occur

Our own Galaxy, the Milky Way galaxy, has a spiral structure, and contains about 200,000 million stars. The spiral disc is about 100,000 light years across.

in groups. Small groups may contain about ten galaxies, while larger groups contain several thousand, some of them almost touching each other.

All galaxies and stars are condensed from matter which was originally scattered in space. The matter was probably distributed unevenly, and galaxies tended to form where it was densest. A dense accumulation becomes even denser as gravitational forces acting between the pieces of matter gradually pull them in towards their centre. Immense clouds of contracting gas formed into galaxies, while, within this cloud, individual stars were being formed where the gas was densest.

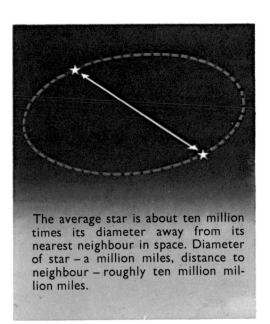

The average star is about ten million times its diameter away from its nearest neighbour in space. Diameter of star – a million miles, distance to neighbour – roughly ten million million miles.

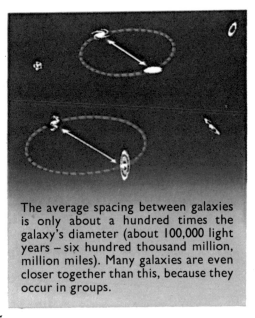

The average spacing between galaxies is only about a hundred times the galaxy's diameter (about 100,000 light years – six hundred thousand million, million miles). Many galaxies are even closer together than this, because they occur in groups.

How to tell the age of a galaxy

1. **Colour.** If the galaxy appears reddish, then it is probably an older galaxy, containing stars which have gone through their evolutionary process very slowly. The stars are of smaller mass than the Sun, and they eventually expand into red giant stars. If the galaxy is blue, it probably contains very hot young stars, which evolve quickly and soon fizzle out.

2. **Spectrum.** The spectrum of the galaxy may reveal the particular kind of star present. Different forms of star have their special types of spectrum. Once the prominent type of star is known, it may be possible to tell its age.

3. **Mass of the galaxy.** This is found, indirectly, from the speed of rotation.

4. **Luminosity.** This is a measure of the light output of a galaxy. Mass divided by luminosity gives an indication of how long the galaxy can be expected to sustain this energy output (i.e. how old it is).

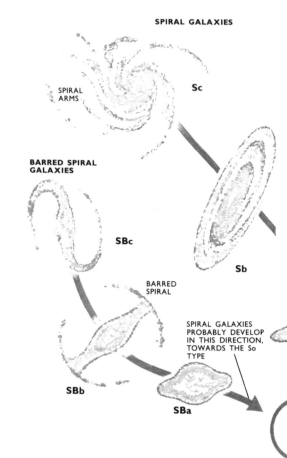

SPIRAL GALAXIES

SPIRAL ARMS

Sc

BARRED SPIRAL GALAXIES

SBc

Sb

BARRED SPIRAL

SPIRAL GALAXIES PROBABLY DEVELOP IN THIS DIRECTION, TOWARDS THE So TYPE

SBb

SBa

Only part of the contracting cloud of gas formed into stars. The remaining gas settled into a flattened disc. Most galaxies apparently start as a whirling cloud of matter, and they do not seem to lose their rotation. More stars eventually form in the disc. They are younger than the stars which condensed when the galaxy first contracted.

The Barred Spirals

The reason for the central straight bar of these galaxies is not completely understood. It is thought to be due to an even balance between magnetic forces in the galaxy and rotational forces. Barred spirals are divided into three groups, a, b and c.

The Grouping of Galaxies

It is possible to distinguish between old stars and young stars, and astronomers are fairly confident that they can estimate the age of any individual star. Galaxies, however, present a more difficult problem. They occur in many different shapes, sizes and colours. Some are powerful emitters of radio waves, while others send out

The Ellipticals

These range from the almost spherical E0 type, which can be hardly rotating at all, to the elliptical E7 type, apparently rotating much more. The more spherical the galaxy, the redder it appears. Ellipticals are thought to be old galaxies. There is very little hydrogen gas and dust between the stars in these galaxies.

The Spirals

Spiral galaxies are thought to form without central bars when the magnetic forces are insignificant compared with the forces associated with the galaxy's rotation. a, b and c denote the importance of the central nucleus relative to the spiral arms. Galaxies with small nuclei (type Sc) tend to have a marked spiral structure. In galaxies with larger nuclei (types Sa and Sb), the spiral structure tends to be more insignificant.

Irregular galaxies

4% of the galaxies did not fit into Hubble's three-pronged system of classification. They are called 'irregulars'. On average, they are smaller than elliptical galaxies.

The So Galaxy

A new type of galaxy is apparently the connecting point between the three main types of galaxy. It is similar to the E-type galaxies, because it has no spiral structure, but is a more flattened ellipse than the E7 type.

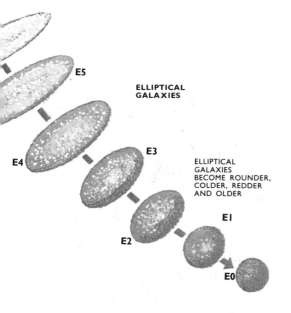

Sa

E7

E5

E4

ELLIPTICAL GALAXIES

E3

ELLIPTICAL GALAXIES BECOME ROUNDER, COLDER, REDDER AND OLDER

E2

E1

E0

hardly any radio waves at all. It is not known for sure which are the old ones and which are the young ones. Edwin Hubble (1889-1953) classified the galaxies according to their structure. He found there are three main types: *elliptical, spiral* and *barred spiral.* About 60% of all galaxies are spirals, 18% are barred spirals, 18% are elliptical, and the remaining 4%, which fit into none of the three main types, are called *irregular.* These have no definite shape at all.

In elliptical galaxies the stars are mainly reddish, and there is very little dust and other matter in between the individual stars. The giant red stars in elliptical galaxies are thought to be old. Most groups of galaxies are predominated by a large elliptical galaxy in their middle.

Stars found in the discs of spiral galaxies are mainly blue. They are thought to be hotter, shorter-lived younger stars. One explanation for this is that galaxies originally formed as spirals. Blue giant stars were formed, but after they died the long-lived red giants remained. By some means, the galaxy then condensed into the form of a reddish ellipse.

CHAPTER TWENTY-FOUR

The Age and Origin of the Universe

OUR OWN GALAXY is like one of millions of spots painted on an expanding balloon. Each of the other spots represents another galaxy. When the balloon is blown up, the surface stretches, and the spots become farther apart. Anyone sitting on one spot on the balloon would think that all the other spots were receding away from him. It seems as though his spot is at the centre of the expansion, but this is an illusion. Anyone on any of the other spots would have exactly the same feeling of being at the centre.

Astronomers have found that all the other galaxies are travelling away from our own galaxy. Distant galaxies recede more quickly than near galaxies. The most distant galaxies so far observed are found to be travelling away at half the speed of light. So, in the past, these galaxies must have been much closer together.

The Big Bang

According to one theory of the origin of the Universe, the *Big Bang Theory*, all the matter in the Universe was originally concentrated together into a *primaeval atom* a hundred million miles in diameter. Between ten and twenty thousand million years ago the atom exploded, and the Universe started its balloon-like expansion.

Some parts of the primaeval atom were flung out more quickly than others. These are now the distant galaxies, and they are still travelling quicker than the nearer galaxies. Astronomers can work out how quickly each galaxy is travelling. They also know how distant the galaxies are. So, by assuming that the galaxies have always been expanding at their present rate, they can work out when the expansion began.

The 'Big Bang' theory predicts a bright beginning (*left*) and a dull end (*right*) to the Universe. But according to the steady state theory (*insets*) the Universe as a whole stays the same.

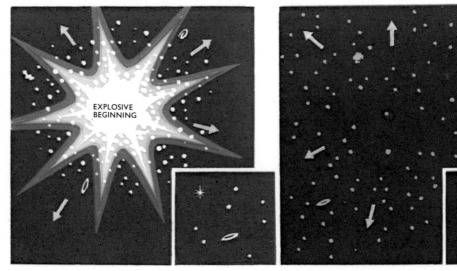

EXPLOSIVE
BEGINNING

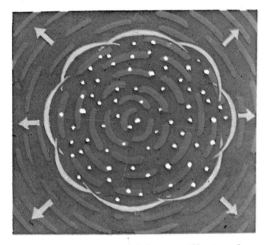

The Red Shift

Light from distant galaxies is examined with a spectroscope. This spreads out the light according to its wavelength. There are two important breaks in the spectrum. A break indicates that this particular wavelength of light is missing – it has been absorbed by cooler gas surrounding the galaxy.

The spectra of near galaxies show that the two breaks are almost in the ultra-violet, but when they occur in the spectra of distant galaxies, they are in the blue, green or even yellow part of the spectrum. They are shifted towards the red end of the spectrum, implying an *increase* in their wavelength.

The *red shift* is thought to be due to the Döppler effect, the increase in wavelength brought about when the source of light is moving away. This is why astronomers believe that all galaxies are receding away from the Earth.

The Universe could be oscillating between periods of expansion *(above)* when the stars and galaxies condense, and periods of contraction *(below)* when the stars explode and fling their matter back into space.

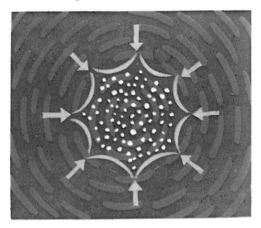

It has a definite age and a definite size.

Unfortunately, this does not provide a very convenient answer. Astronomers are almost certain that some galaxies are at least ten thousand million years old, and the age of the Universe (assuming that the expansion rate is constant) comes to only about eight thousand million years. One way of getting round this discrepancy assumes that the expansion rate was slower in the initial stages. When the Universe was just beginning to expand matter was packed more closely together, and the gravitational force attracting the pieces of matter towards each other was correspondingly greater. As the force of the explosion pushed them farther apart, the gravitational force was reduced, and the expansion speeded up. .

According to the 'big bang' theory, the Universe is changing all the time.

The Steady State Theory

There is very little doubt that the Universe is expanding like a balloon, and that existing galaxies (spots on the balloon) are becoming farther apart. But in spite of this, a rival theory of the Universe suggests that the Universe as a whole is not changing at all. Individual stars and galaxies of stars evolve and die, but new ones are being continually born to replace them. While the amount of space between existing galaxies increases, new matter is being created in the space. The amount of matter created is enough to keep the average density of galaxies in the Universe constant. If this is so, the Universe had no definite beginning, and will have no definite end. It has no definite size, either, for it stretches out to infinity.

How can matter be created in empty space, to keep the average density of matter in the Universe constant? The answer is that there must be another kind of field in space — similar to gravitational fields, or magnetic fields, but capable of producing matter from energy in space. No such field has ever been detected, but this is no reason for stating definitely that none exists. The field has not to produce very many particles — the steady state theory requires only one hydrogen atom to be produced per litre every few thousand million years.

The Oscillating Universe

According to another possible theory, the Universe is oscillating between periods of expansion and periods of contraction. Stars form during the expansion period, and collapse during the contraction. At present, we would be in the middle of an expansion period. But sooner or later the expanding bubble would start to deflate. This theory may be possible, but it is not very likely.

Checking the Theories

There are a great many possible theories of the formation of the Uni-

The Big Bang theory. The Primaeval atom, 100 million light years across, explodes. It contains protons, neutrons and electrons, all the building bricks necessary to make atoms. Soon after the bang, the temperature within the Primaeval atom is 1,000 million degrees, and particles start joining together to form atomic nuclei

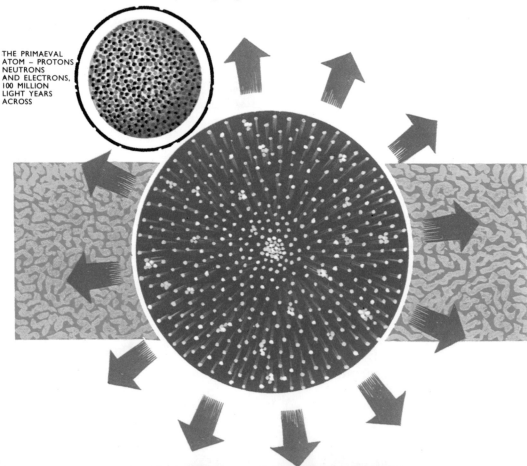

THE PRIMAEVAL
ATOM — PROTONS
NEUTRONS
AND ELECTRONS,
100 MILLION
LIGHT YEARS
ACROSS

After about 30 million years, the temperature had dropped to a few thousand degrees. Chance accumulations of matter started to condense to form stars and galaxies. The Universe of today is shown above. It is about ten thousand million years old. Parts of the Primaeval atom which were given the greatest velocities in the explosion are now farthest from the centre.

verse. It is impossible, from the observational facts available, to decide definitely on any one of them. The difficulty is that we cannot see far enough back in space and time. Light from distant galaxies takes time to travel from them to the Earth. The most distant galaxies yet discovered are about five thousand million light years away — that is, light takes five thousand million years to travel from the galaxy to the Earth, and we are really observing what happened five thousand million years ago.

The main battle lies between the big bang and the steady state theories. Each predicts a different distribution of the brightness of the galaxy with distance. While both theories are in agreement for the nearer stars, they diverge when distances become greater and the apparent brightness (as seen from the Earth) decreases. It can be shown that the steady state Universe predicts a falling off- of brightness with distance greater than the simple exploding Universe. This can be checked using radio telescopes which are more sensitive than optical telescopes for very distant galaxies. The results so far obtained are slightly in favour of the Big Bang Theory.

CHAPTER TWENTY-FIVE

Olbers' Paradox

IS THE Universe infinite, or does it end somewhere, with completely empty space and nothingness beyond? Heinrich Olbers (1758-1840), a German astronomer, thought he had found an answer to the question.

He argued that if the nearby parts of the Universe were a typical sample, repeated again and again in more distant parts, then it would be impossible for the Universe to be infinitely large. If it were, it would contain an infinitely large number of stars and galaxies. Each star radiates light, and no matter how far away the star is, some of its light reaches the Earth. The argument continues: if the Earth were receiving light from all directions from an infinite number of stars, then the night sky would appear blindingly bright. In every direction there was bound to be a star. The sky would appear to be an unbroken source of light. Yet the night sky is definitely dark, so according to Olbers, there cannot be an infinite number of stars, and the Universe must be bounded.

The great flaw in this argument came with the discovery that all distant galaxies are receding away from our own galaxy (this fact is shown by the *red shift* in their spectra). The more distant they are, the faster their speed or recession; some observed galaxies are receding at half the speed of light (i.e. at 93,000 miles per second). It seems likely that there are more distant galaxies, travelling at about the speed of light. Astronomers on Earth will never be able to detect these galaxies, because their light *will never reach the Earth.*

The galaxies could stretch out to infinity. Light from the most distant ones would never contribute to the brightness of the night sky.

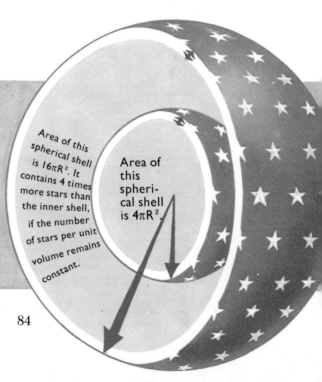

Olbers divided the Universe into a series of very thin concentric shells, surrounding the Earth. The illumination on Earth from the shells falls off as the square of the radius. But the illumination also depends on the number of stars in the shell, i.e. it increases as the square of the radius. In other words, illumination does not depend on R at all – it is constant. So each shell contributes a certain, constant amount of illumination. An infinite number of shells contribute an infinite amount of illumination.

Area of this spherical shell is $16\pi R^2$. It contains 4 times more stars than the inner shell, if the number of stars per unit volume remains constant.

Area of this spherical shell is $4\pi R^2$.

CHAPTER TWENTY-SIX

Relativity

LIGHT TRAVELS at 186,000 miles per second through empty space. No matter who measures it, where they are, or how fast they are moving at the time, they will always get the same answer for the velocity of light through a vacuum. Someone on Earth, measuring the velocity of light reaching the Earth from the Sun, would get exactly the same result as someone on a space-ship, measuring the velocity of light from the Sun while his space-ship travelled away from the Solar System at almost the speed of light.

To the observer on Earth, the space-ship would apparently be travelling with the light waves. If it were travelling at half the velocity of light (93,000 miles per second) it is reasonable to suppose that the velocity of light, *relative* to the space-ship, is only 93,000 miles per second. For this is the way velocities, or *relative velocities*, usually behave. For example, if a train is moving at 60 miles per hour, and a car is moving in the same direction at 30 miles per hour, then the train is gaining 30 miles each hour on the car. Their *relative velocity* is 30 miles an hour. The measured velocity, or *relative velocity*, of any moving object depends on the movement of the person who is measuring the velocity.

However, these rules never apply to light waves, and light is different from all material objects in this respect. According to the observer on Earth, the observer in the space-ship should get a different answer if he were to measure the velocity of

light—but he does not. The reason, according to the Theory of Relativity, is that he is using a different timing system, and the 'yard-stick' he is using to measure the distance light travels in a second is a different length from the same 'yard-stick' on Earth. Velocities are measured by finding the time interval taken to travel a definite distance (velocity is equal to distance divided by time).

The observer in the space-ship has been able to work out that light travels 186,000 miles each second because (1) his 'yard-stick' appears, relatively, shorter than the one on Earth, and (2) his clock has been going more slowly. Seconds take relatively longer on the moving clock.

The exact amount by which distances are, relatively, shrunk, and

ALBERT EINSTEIN
(1879 – 1955)

time is, relatively, drawn out was calculated by Albert Einstein in his famous Theory of Relativity. The first part of the theory, the Special Theory, which appeared in 1905, was entirely based on one new idea, the constancy of the velocity of light (through empty space) for all observers.

The other starting point, or axiom, of the Special Theory was already accepted by most physicists. This states that nothing is absolutely at rest. The observer on Earth may believe that he is at rest and the man in the space-ship is moving away from him. But the man in the space-ship is equally justified in thinking that he is stationary, and the Earth is receding from him. Technically, there is no difference between the two viewpoints.

Building his theory on just these two axioms, Einstein found the factor

$$\sqrt{1 - \frac{V^2}{C^2}}$$

creeping into many of the equations. V is the velocity on the space-ship and C is the velocity of light. If the observer on Earth could compare his 'yard-stick' with the moving 'yard-stick' in the space-ship, he would find the moving 'yard-stick' was shorter by this factor. If the space-ship were travelling at half the velocity of light, the 'yard-stick' would measure only about 31 inches (although the space-man himself would still believe it to be a full yard long). At seven-eighths of the velocity of light, the 'yard-stick' would measure only 17½ inches, and, if the space-ship were capable of reaching the velocity of light, the 'yard-stick' would shrink so that it was infinitely small.

The difficulty about what would happen if the space-ship travelled faster than light does not arise, for another of Einstein's conclusions was that nothing could ever travel as fast as light.

A similar factor appeared in Einstein's time equations. While clocks on Earth take one second to record one second, a moving clock travelling with half the velocity of light takes 1·15 Earth seconds to record one 'moving clock' second. A space-man, embarking on a trip that lasts for 100 Earth years, would find that he ages far less during the trip. If he had been travelling with nine-tenths of the velocity of light, he would think he had spent only 43 years in space when

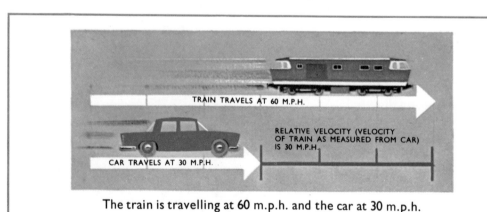

TRAIN TRAVELS AT 60 M.P.H.

CAR TRAVELS AT 30 M.P.H.

RELATIVE VELOCITY (VELOCITY OF TRAIN AS MEASURED FROM CAR) IS 30 M.P.H.

The train is travelling at 60 m.p.h. and the car at 30 m.p.h.

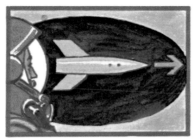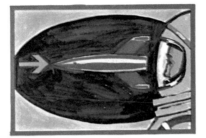

The man in the first space-ship thinks the second is moving forwards.
The second thinks the first is moving backwards. They have no means
of knowing who is right.

he returned. For something moving
with the velocity of light, time passes
infinitely slowly. As time varies with
velocity, it is possible to 'travel in
time'.

Distances and times are not the
only things to be affected. Mass (the
amount of matter in an object) does
not stay the same when the object
moves faster. The mass increases with
the velocity, and if it were possible to
make the object move at 186,000
miles per second, its mass would
become infinitely large.

From these equations came the
famous relationship between mass
and energy. The amount of energy
associated with mass is equal to the
product of the mass and the velocity of light squared ($E = mc^2$). This
amount of energy is released whenever a tiny amount of matter is 'lost'
in a nuclear reactor.

When it was first proposed, there
was no means of verifying Einstein's
conclusions in the Special Theory.
The one 'proof' at hand showed only
that his assumption about the velocity of light was not wrong. A few
years earlier, two physicists, Michel-
son and Morley, had measured the
velocity of light in two different directions at the same time, hoping to get
different results (they would have

been measuring *relative* velocities of
light). They found no difference at all.

Better proof has been obtained
from experiments in nuclear physics.
Small atomic particles are accelerated
in huge machines by electromagnetic
and electrostatic forces until they
have a velocity approaching the velocity of light. In one machine, the
cyclotron, the particles are accelerated at regular intervals. In between

The Special Theory

The Special Theory starts off
with the assumptions that:
1. No-one is absolutely at
rest. 2. The velocity of light
is the same measured by all
observers.

It follows from these that
a 'stationary' observer
thinks: 1. A moving yard-
stick is shortened in its
direction of movement. 2. A
moving clock goes slower
than his clock. 3. The mass
of moving objects increases
as their velocity increases.
4. No object can move as
fast as light.

None of these effects is
large enough to be noticed
until the velocities involved
are about a tenth of the
velocity of light (i.e. 18,600
miles per second).

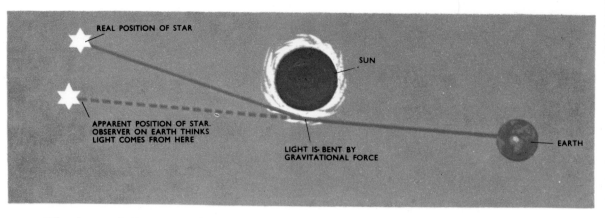

REAL POSITION OF STAR

SUN

APPARENT POSITION OF STAR.
OBSERVER ON EARTH THINKS
LIGHT COMES FROM HERE

LIGHT IS· BENT BY
GRAVITATIONAL FORCE

EARTH

The General Theory predicts that light should be bent by the gravitational force of the Sun. This alters the star's apparent position.

accelerations they travel in circles around the cyclotron. According to the old ideas of dynamics, the time taken to travel the curved path should be constant. But the masses of the particles increase relativistically, so they are slowed down. Because they are slowed down, they arrive too late to be accelerated. The regular accelerations are missed and the particles slow down still more, as predicted by the Special Theory.

LIFT ACCELERATES
DOWN

FORCE CAUSED
BY ACCELERAT
ION

UP

DOWN

FORCE OF
GRAVITY

The starting point of the General Theory. Forces produce accelerations, and accelerations produce 'forces'.

Relativistic differences in time, too, have been measured in nuclear physics experiments. Some minute particles ejected in nuclear explosions cannot live very long, and they soon 'decay' into something else. But when the experiments have been made with particles travelling at very high velocities (for instance the particles arriving at the Earth in the form of cosmic rays) they appear to live longer before decaying. Time has been stretched out for them, in a relativistic manner.

In the Special Theory, Einstein had tackled only part of the problem. Situations were simplified because all the moving objects were either at 'rest' or moving with constant velocity. It is a more complicated problem when the velocity changes (in other words, when the object accelerates or decelerates). This was dealt with in the enlarged General Theory of Relativity, put forward in 1916, eleven years after the Special Theory.

The basic idea in this theory was the great similarity between the force of gravity and an accelerating force. Someone going down in a lift, and being accelerated downwards,

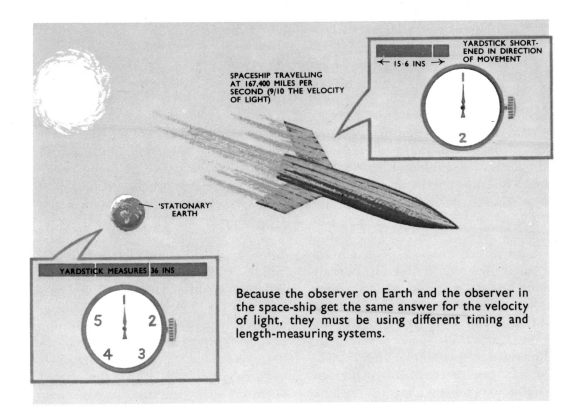

SPACESHIP TRAVELLING AT 167,400 MILES PER SECOND (9/10 THE VELOCITY OF LIGHT)

YARDSTICK SHORT-ENED IN DIRECTION OF MOVEMENT

← 15·6 INS →

'STATIONARY' EARTH

YARDSTICK MEASURES 36 INS

Because the observer on Earth and the observer in the space-ship get the same answer for the velocity of light, they must be using different timing and length-measuring systems.

feels his stomach has been left behind. Because he is accelerating, he is experiencing an upward force, and this is partially counteracting the downward force of gravity. These two kinds of forces are equivalent.

The mathematical equations involved in the General Theory are exceedingly complex, and the theory is more difficult to verify than the Special Theory. One of the predictions made in the General Theory was that light, like lumps of matter, could be attracted towards other lumps of matter by gravitational forces. Light rays are bent when they pass near huge bodies like the Sun.

If the Sun is near the direct line from a distant star to the Earth, light rays from the star are bent so that the apparent position of the star shifts slightly. Normally the Sun is radiating so much light of its own that the light from the star is 'lost' in it. But during eclipses of the Sun, most of the Sun's radiation is blotted out, and nearby stars can be seen. When their positions are measured accurately, they are found to be slightly different from the real positions, and the amount of shift agrees very well with the amount of shift predicted in Einstein's equations.

CHAPTER TWENTY-SEVEN

The Curvature of Space

WHAT IS THE shape of the Universe? Is it cubical, spherical, or completely unbounded, stretching out to infinity? All the information we have about the extremities of the Universe comes from the light (and radio waves) radiated by distant galaxies. Light seems to reach the earth from all directions, so perhaps the Universe is symmetrical, either spherical or infinite. But the Universe is neither of these. It cannot be represented fully by any three-dimensional geometrical figure. The outside boundary of the Universe cannot be pictured because light is not bringing its information in straight lines. All the space inside the boundary is *curved*.

Space is not three-dimensional, like a building block or a sphere. It is four-dimensional, and the fourth dimension is *time*. It appears in equations governing the properties of space, but there is no way of picturing it.

Space is curved and distorted because it contains matter—all the billions of billions of stars and galaxies in the Universe. Light is affected by the gravitational forces exerted by matter in space. Over long distances, light travels in curves instead of straight lines. Our own Sun is not a particularly massive star, but even it can produce a detectable bending in light coming from a distant star to the Earth, if the light passes within a few degrees of the Sun.

The direction of bending observed seems to suggest that light bends *inwards*. A light ray starting out from any point in the Universe is, on the whole, attracted in towards the centre all the time. Eventually, after being attracted inwards by all the matter in the Universe, the light ray will eventually arrive back at its starting point. It is like travelling in a straight line away from any point on Earth. The 'straight line' turns out to be a curved path around the Earth's surface. Every 25,000 miles (the Earth's circumference) the path arrives back at its starting point, having formed a *great circle*.

The curvature of space can be pictured by the odd behaviour of light—in particular by the *velocity of light*. Velocity is distance divided by time. An illustration including the behavi-

The uncurved universe. Time is not needed to define it—it could be pictured in three dimensions. The universe would not be curved if light travelled in straight lines.

STAR

SUN   EARTH

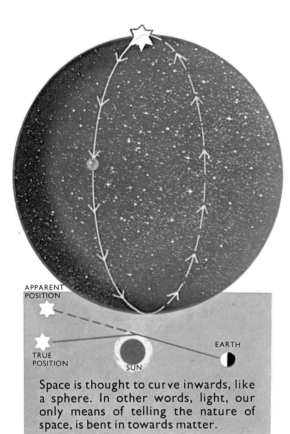

APPARENT POSITION

TRUE POSITION

EARTH

SUN

Space is thought to curve inwards, like a sphere. In other words, light, our only means of telling the nature of space, is bent in towards matter.

Albert Einstein's relativity theories are all tied up with the behaviour of the velocity of light. In his General Theory of Relativity (1916) Einstein showed what would happen if light interacted with matter. There were three possibilities in his equations: either light was unaffected, in which case the Universe would be 'flat', or light could be bent either inwards or outwards. Both these second and third possibilities would produce a curved, four-dimensional space. But if light curved outwards instead of inwards, the diagram would become saddle-shaped and the curves hyperbolae instead of circles. Light rays would fly outwards and never return to their starting point. Present experimental evidence seems to favour the inwards-curving space.

our of the velocity of light also includes the dimension of time (which is impossible to include in any purely spatial diagram).

If light is unaffected by matter, and always travels in straight lines (i.e. at the same velocity) space is undistorted and uncurved. This can be pictured as a flat, two-dimensional surface (this is a way of saving the third dimension until it is really needed).

If light doubles back on itself on a great circle route around the Universe, the two dimensional diagram turns into a three-dimensional sphere. The paths of light are circles around the sphere. The light changes its direction so its *velocity* changes (velocity takes into account direction as well as speed).

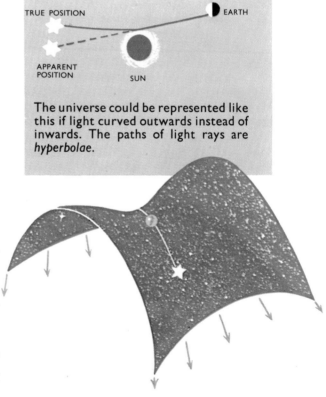

TRUE POSITION

EARTH

APPARENT POSITION

SUN

The universe could be represented like this if light curved outwards instead of inwards. The paths of light rays are *hyperbolae.*

CHAPTER TWENTY-EIGHT

Mapping the Stars

IN ORDER to record exactly where each star is at a certain time, astronomers pretend that its light makes a spot on an imaginary spherical screen surrounding the Earth which they call the *celestial sphere*. It is not difficult to imagine such a sphere; you get this impression yourself when looking at the night sky. But from any point on the Earth's surface you can only see part of the celestial sphere; the sky appears to be a great dome, or inverted bowl, studded with stars.

In order to fix the position of a town on the surface of the Earth, imaginary lines of reference are used. Lines of latitude circle the Earth parallel to the equator, while lines of longitude run from pole to pole and cut the lines of latitude at right-angles. In this way, the whole global surface is divided up into little 'squares'. Astronomers use exactly the same method in order to fix the position of stars upon the celestial sphere. The celestial North and South

A simple polar map projection. The shadows of the lines of latitude and longitude cast by the bulb upon the paper form the basis of a map. The same principle could be employed to produce a simple map of part of the night sky.

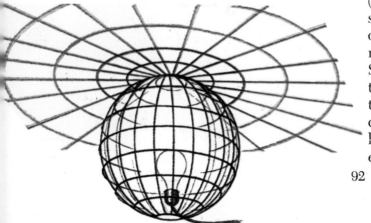

Poles are points immediately above the Earth's North and South poles, while the celestial equator, just like the Earth's equator, is a line circling the sphere midway between the two poles. Lines of latitude and longitude are used, too, but they go under different names. Lines of latitude are called *declination circles* on the celestial sphere, though the difference is in name only and the position of a star of declination 55° N. corresponds exactly to the position of a point on the Earth whose latitude is 55° N. Owing to the spin of the Earth this means that the star passes directly over every point on the Earth's surface whose latitude is 55° N. once per day (really, every such point passes directly beneath the star).

The word corresponding to longitude is *right ascension*. Just as there must be some point from which longitude is measured on the Earth (it happens to be Greenwich, London) so there must be a point from which to measure right ascension on the celestial sphere. This is called the *First Point of Aries*. To understand the position of the First Point of Aries you have to imagine the Earth's equator extended like a great tilted plate ('tilted' because the Earth does not spin in an upright position in its orbit around the Sun). As the Earth makes its annual journey around the Sun there are just two points where the surface of this tilted plate points towards the Sun (i.e. where the midday sun appears to be directly overhead to a person standing on the equator). These are called the *equi-*

noxes and occur on March 21st and September 21st. The former is the First Point of Aries. Right ascension is not measured as so many degrees east or west of this point, as longitude is from Greenwich; instead, it is measured westwards all the way round. Moreover, it is not even measured in degrees but in *hours,* going from 0 to 24 hours.

Any star's position may be given in terms of these co-ordinates. For instance, in 1950 the co-ordinates of Sirius, the Dog star, were: declination 16° 38' South, right ascension 6 hours 43·0 minutes. The year has to be mentioned for a number of reasons. The time at which the equinoxes occur, for instance, changes by about three seconds each year (hence the First Point of Aries does too) because the Earth's axis is wobbling around in a slow circle. And then the so-called 'fixed stars' are not quite fixed but have a very slight motion.

For convenience in identification, the stars are divided into groups called *constellations.* But it must be remembered that although two stars may look to be very close together when viewed from the Earth, one may be many millions of miles in front of, or behind, its apparent neighbour.

The constellations were given names by the Greeks, Romans, Arabs and others many years ago and most of these names still persist, though there are also one or two modern constellations. The brighter stars were given names of their own, but for normal description they are given Greek letters. Thus, the principal star in the constellation Canis Major (Sirius) is known as Alpha (α) Canis Majoris. The next brightest star is Beta (β), the next brightest Gamma

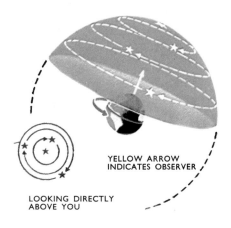

YELLOW ARROW INDICATES OBSERVER

LOOKING DIRECTLY ABOVE YOU

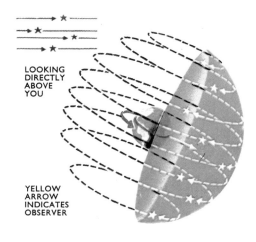

LOOKING DIRECTLY ABOVE YOU

YELLOW ARROW INDICATES OBSERVER

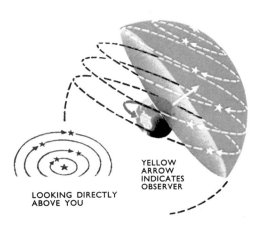

YELLOW ARROW INDICATES OBSERVER

LOOKING DIRECTLY ABOVE YOU

The apparent motion of the stars to an observer at the north pole *(top),* to an observer at the equator *(middle)* and to an observer in mid-latitudes *(bottom).*

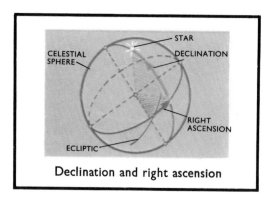

CELESTIAL SPHERE
STAR
DECLINATION
RIGHT ASCENSION
ECLIPTIC

Declination and right ascension

(γ), and so on. Faint stars are indicated usually merely by numbers.

Time and Time Measurement

The position of the heavenly bodies is of great importance in the measurement of time, for time can only be measured in relation to other happenings. If, for example, there were no Sun, then we should not have a 'day' or a 'year' as we know it. And if there were no Moon there would be no such thing as a month. To divide time up into units that can be measured, Man must have some external source of comparison. The obvious ones which occurred to early

The celestial sphere, showing how the position of a star corresponds to a relative position on the surface of the Earth.

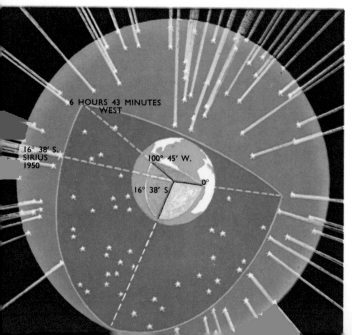

6 HOURS 43 MINUTES WEST

16° 38' S.
SIRIUS
1950

100° 45' W.

16° 38' S

0°

Man were the regular rising and setting of the Sun, the waxing and waning of the Moon and the cycle of the seasons. As men learnt more about the heavens they also noticed that certain stars changed their position with relation to other stars at fixed intervals. So, the earliest divisions of time were into nights and days, measured by the rising and setting of the Sun; into months, measured by the waxing and waning of the Moon; and into years, measured by the seasons. This seems very simple on the face of it, but in fact days, months and years are an ill-assorted trio which have led to great confusion in past calendars.

A *solar day* is the time taken for a point on the spinning globe to make what appears to be one revolution and come back to its original position facing the Sun. Really, this is slightly more than just one revolution, for by the time the point has revolved back to where it started, it is not facing the Sun as it should be. This is due to the fact that the Earth has meanwhile moved on one and a half *million* miles in its orbit around the Sun. Thus, the point must revolve a little more in order to 'look back' at the Sun.

The *sidereal day* (star day) is also based upon one revolution of the Earth, but in this case the starting point is measured to a distant star. The stars are so far away that the Earth moves very little in relation to them, and after one complete revolution the point directly faces the star again. No 'extra turn' is necessary in this case. Thus, a sidereal day is a little shorter than a solar day (the difference between them is about four minutes).

The solar day, which is measured by a sundial, is called *apparent time*.

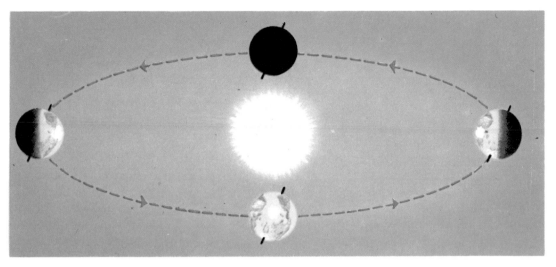

A year is the time taken by the Earth to complete one orbit of the Sun (a little more than 365 days).

It would not be very convenient to use apparent time for everyday measurements because the solar day differs in length throughout the year. This is due to the fact that the Earth's orbit is elliptical in shape, with the Sun not quite in the centre. The Earth travels more quickly when it is in *perihelion* (nearest the Sun) than when it is in *aphelion* (farthest from the Sun).

The day we measure by our clocks, unlike the natural day measured by the Sun, is constant in length. We call this the *mean solar day,* for it is the uniform average of the total length of solar days.

It would be very convenient if a year, which is the time the Earth takes to make one complete orbit of the Sun, worked out to an exact number of days (spins of the Earth). Unfortunately, the time taken is 365·2422 days, but since this is a most impracticable figure our 'year' neglects the odd fraction of a day. This is why every fourth year is called a leap year. The extra day in a leap year (366 instead of 365) allows for the extra fraction of a day in that year and at the same time compensates for the fractions of a day left over from the three preceding years (and even then it is not quite right).

Round the Earth circles its own satellite, the Moon. The time taken by the Moon to complete one orbit of the Earth, about 27½ days (Earth spins), is called a *lunar month.* The Moon makes roughly thirteen orbits of the Earth in the time the Earth takes to make one orbit of the Sun. But a simple calculation shows that the lunar month does not fit exactly thirteen times into the 365-day year and it cannot be used as a standard and unalterable division of the calendar. In fact, you will find that the waxing and waning of the Moon bears little relation to our present 'months'. If months divided into an exact number of days, and years into an exact number of months, calendars would be much simpler.

CHAPTER TWENTY-NINE

The Planetarium

OVER THE CENTURIES many people have tried to make models of the motions of the planets and the stars. In the 17th and 18th centuries mechanical models of the solar system called *orreries* were popular. These mechanisms were designed so that, by turning a handle, different sized globes representing the planets revolved around a central sun, in times proportional to the planetary periods of revolution. Other methods of copying the heavenly motions were tried but, until the invention of the planetarium in 1926, none could give a representation of what we actually see when we look up at the sky.

A few cities in the world are lucky enough to have a planetarium. Being inside the planetarium is truly like sitting out under the real stars.

The night sky is projected onto a dome by a giant precision projecting instrument like a dumb-bell in the centre—weighing 2½ tons and containing 29,000 individual parts. This instrument can be turned in three different directions on its bearings and so can show the night sky as it appears from any latitude on Earth in any century past or future.

One round end of the dumb-bell is the *Northern Star Projector* and contains 16 projecting lenses for all the stars in the Northern Hemisphere. The other end when turned up contains 16 projecting lenses for the stars in the Southern Hemisphere. All told, 8,900 stars of 65 different brightnesses are projected. Since each projector has 1/16 of the ceiling allotted to it, this mosaic of star projections must be fitted so that no two parts overlap.

The stars are projected from *star plates* behind each of the 16 projecting lenses. In earlier models these were sheets of copper foil with 65 different sized holes punched in them to represent the different star magnitudes, but nowadays a film is used instead. These star plates are specially made up and are not just photographs of the night sky. Allowance has to be made on them for the fact that neither end of the dumb-bell is

A mechanical model of the solar system called an *orrery*. Pluto, discovered in 1930, is not represented in the model.

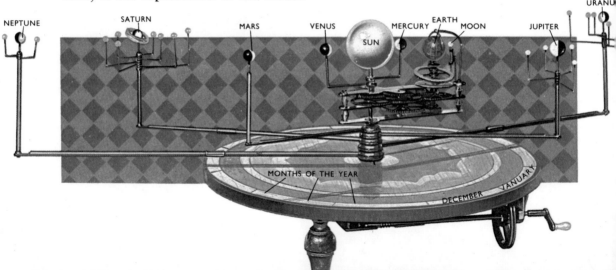

NEPTUNE SATURN MARS VENUS SUN MERCURY EARTH MOON JUPITER URANUS

MONTHS OF THE YEAR

DECEMBER JANUARY

ever in the centre of the dome. Attached to the instrument are other types of individual projectors for the vague blur of the Milky Way, the nebulae and the variable stars.

As the giant instrument moves silently on its bearings, it simulates the three basic movements of the Earth, the vantage point from which we look at the sky. Our planet rotates once a day—the *diurnal motion*. It travels around the Sun in an approximately circular path once every year —the *annual motion*. And the axis of the Earth describes a slow wobbling circle—the *precessional motion*. A number of motors of various fixed speeds turn the instrument so that these motions can be shown. The motors can be coupled together or run separately.

The images of the moving Sun, Moon and planets come from the projectors in the cage-like skeleton framework of each limb of the instrument. Saturn, the Sun and the Moon are in the northern limb, and Jupiter, Mars, Venus and Mercury in the southern half. There are no moving projectors for the outer planets which are too faint to be seen.

There are two projecting lamps for each planet and the Sun, mounted alongside each other. This is only to prevent blocking out of the light by the arms of the supporting framework. The two images from these lamps coincide on the dome. Each planetary projector is driven around the long axis (the line joining the dumb-bells) in its correct period of revolution by gears connected to an axle running up inside the framework. This is not sufficient though, because the revolution of the planets is watched from an Earth which is also revolving about the Sun.

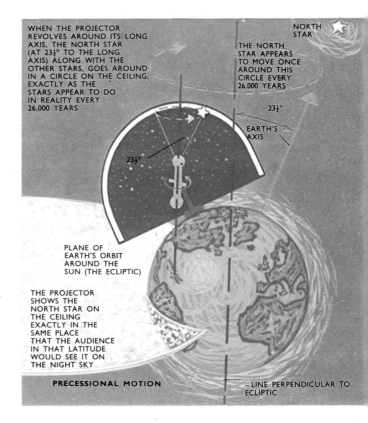

WHEN THE PROJECTOR REVOLVES AROUND ITS LONG AXIS, THE NORTH STAR (AT 23½° TO THE LONG AXIS) ALONG WITH THE OTHER STARS, GOES AROUND IN A CIRCLE ON THE CEILING, EXACTLY AS THE STARS APPEAR TO DO IN REALITY EVERY 26,000 YEARS

NORTH STAR

THE NORTH STAR APPEARS TO MOVE ONCE AROUND THIS CIRCLE EVERY 26,000 YEARS

23½°

EARTH'S AXIS

23½°

PLANE OF EARTH'S ORBIT AROUND THE SUN (THE ECLIPTIC)

THE PROJECTOR SHOWS THE NORTH STAR ON THE CEILING EXACTLY IN THE SAME PLACE THAT THE AUDIENCE IN THAT LATITUDE WOULD SEE IT ON THE NIGHT SKY

PRECESSIONAL MOTION

—LINE PERPENDICULAR TO ECLIPTIC

The dumb-bell rotates around its long axis to show the 26,000 year precession of the Earth's axis.

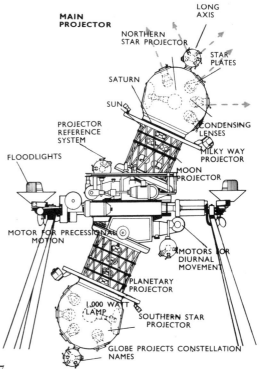

MAIN PROJECTOR

LONG AXIS

NORTHERN STAR PROJECTOR

STAR PLATES

SATURN

SUN

CONDENSING LENSES

PROJECTOR REFERENCE SYSTEM

MILKY WAY PROJECTOR

FLOODLIGHTS

MOON PROJECTOR

MOTOR FOR PRECESSIONAL MOTION

MOTORS FOR DIURNAL MOVEMENT

PLANETARY PROJECTOR

1,000 WATT LAMP

SOUTHERN STAR PROJECTOR

GLOBE PROJECTS CONSTELLATION NAMES

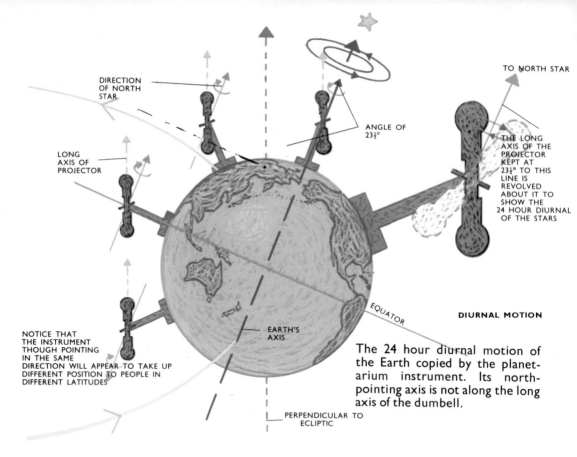

DIRECTION
OF NORTH
STAR

ANGLE OF
23½°

TO NORTH STAR

THE LONG
AXIS OF THE
PROJECTOR
KEPT AT
23½° TO THIS
LINE IS
REVOLVED
ABOUT IT TO
SHOW THE
24 HOUR DIURNAL
OF THE STARS

LONG
AXIS OF
PROJECTOR

EQUATOR

DIURNAL MOTION

EARTH'S
AXIS

NOTICE THAT
THE INSTRUMENT
THOUGH POINTING
IN THE SAME
DIRECTION WILL APPEAR TO TAKE UP
DIFFERENT POSITION TO PEOPLE IN
DIFFERENT LATITUDES

The 24 hour diurnal motion of
the Earth copied by the planetarium instrument. Its north-
pointing axis is not along the long
axis of the dumbell.

PERPENDICULAR TO
ECLIPTIC

Each pair of projectors lies each side of a long rod. One end of this rod (in the compartment for each planet) slides through a pin fixed to a gear wheel representing the period of the Earth's motion. The other end slides on another pin on the planet's gear wheel, turning around the same centre, but not fixed to the same axle. When both of these gear wheels rotate at their respective speeds, the planetary projector slides around backwards and forwards and shines on the dome exactly where the planet appears to be as seen from the Earth.

The line going through the centres of the dumb-bells, i.e. the long axis of the instrument, points perpendicularly to the plane of the Earth's orbit around the Sun (the ecliptic). The Earth's axis pointing to the North Pole star on the dome is represented by another line which is at 23½° to the first one. So, a revolution of the instrument about this line shows the daily or diurnal motion of the stars about the North Pole. The precessional motion is demonstrated by revolving the instrument about the first line, which is kept perpendicular to the ecliptic.

Various devices show unusual effects. Phases of the Moon are produced by a hemispherical cup driven off the motors, which moves over and partly, or completely, covers a concave spotted mirror, from which light is reflected to represent the Moon.

The planetarium is not only of educational and recreational value. There are small planetariums set up in Universities and navigational colleges over the world to instruct students in the various motions of the heavenly bodies seen from our moving Earth.

CHAPTER THIRTY

The Development of the Telescope

THERE IS considerable doubt about who actually invented the telescope. The Italian Giambattista Della Porta mentions in his book, published in 1589, an instrument which uses an arrangement of lenses to make distant objects larger and clearer. But there are no records of anyone having ever seen this instrument. Whatever the truth, the idea of making a telescope was fostered in Italy, but the first telescope was probably made in 1608 in Holland by Hans Lippershey, a spectacle maker of Middelburg. The story is told that one day two children were in his shop playing with some of his lenses. He noticed that when they held two particular lenses in a certain position the weather vane on a nearby church appeared much larger. He mounted the lenses in a tube and sold the invention to the governing body of the Netherlands. The idea spread so rapidly across Europe that by the end of 1609 telescopes were being made in London.

Galileo Galilei heard of the Dutch invention and made a telescope himself by mounting a convex and concave lens in a lead tube so that their principal foci coincided beyond the concave lens. This lens arrangement still bears his name in the *Galilean telescope* and gives an enlarged upright image.

Galileo's interest lay chiefly in the optical properties of his telescopes. He paid very little attention to the mountings. Scheiner designed an instrument called a *helioscope* which used improved mountings. He mounted the telescope frame at the top of a polar axis. At the bottom was a circular dial on which were marked 24 one-hour divisions. The telescope was set by pointing it at the Sun. Then, by rotating the polar axis, the

A reflecting telescope made by Herschel

Foucault's reflecting telescope.

telescope would automatically follow the Sun's path. This was in fact the first *equatorial telescope.*

The Galilean telescope suffered badly from two lens defects, *chromatic* and *spherical aberration.* Chromatic aberration, caused by the glass lenses splitting the light into its component colours, gives rise to images with coloured blurs round the edges. Spherical aberration, caused by the outer parts of the lenses bending the light more sharply than the central zone, further blurs the image unless only the centre of the lens is used, but this means narrowing the field of view and reducing the amount of light entering the telescope.

It was then discovered that by making the telescope lenses with very long focal lengths compared with the size of the aperture, these defects were greatly reduced, and as a consequence telescopes grew to almost unmanageable lengths. Hevelius at Danzig in the mid-17th century made a 150-foot telescope. The lenses were mounted within a wooden framework and the whole thing was awkward to manipulate.

Then Christian Huygens, a Dutch physicist, set about making giant telescopes manageable by one person. He did away with all the wooden tubing, and mounted the objective lens on a grooved pole. By pulling on a cord he could raise or lower the lens. The eyepiece he set up some distance away. Instead of using one lens for an eyepiece, he found that a combination of two gave a clearer image. Although he did not know it, he had invented an *achromatic pair,* a lens combination which eliminates chromatic aberration.

Telescopes continued to grow longer and longer. Obviously some equally powerful but much shorter telescope was needed. In 1663 James Gregory suggested doing this by using a system of mirrors rather than lenses, but although his idea was good he was unable to produce a satisfactory set of mirrors. It was left to Isaac Newton in 1668 to make the first satisfactory *reflecting telescope.* Mirrors have an advantage over lenses in that chromatic aberration is completely avoided, as there is no splitting of the light on reflection.

Scheiner obtaining an inverted image of the Sun on a screen.

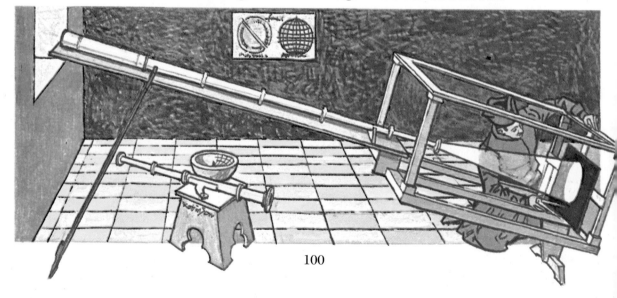

100

Newton's reflecting telescope.

But the early mirrors were far from good. Made from bell metal, an alloy of tin and copper, they needed constant polishing. It was not until two centuries later that Foucault made the first silver-on-glass mirrors. Working on similar lines to the Gregorian telescope, the Frenchman Cassegrain brought out an improved design. His telescope was even shorter than a Gregorian of the same strength, and the mirror combination gave less spherical aberration.

The Gregorian, Cassegrain, and Newtonian designs were good, but for many years, however painstakingly made, the quality of the mirrors was poor.

For a long while the reflecting telescope stayed popular while the refractors, such as the Galilean, lay half forgotten. Their revival began in 1729 when Chester Moor Hall produced an achromatic compound lens by sticking together a concave lens of flint glass and a convex lens of crown glass. A great deal of time, energy and money was then concentrated on producing large pieces of flawless glass suitable for lens making. By the middle of the 19th century most of the telescopes of the day were refractors. Many of them were fitted with clockwork mechanisms so that they could automatically follow the path of their object across the sky.

Nearly all the large modern telescopes are reflectors. The swing back to this type began when Foucault in 1856 made astronomical mirrors by depositing a thin layer of silver on a glass surface. The method he used is still basically the same as that used today. First the surface was so thoroughly cleaned that when it was dipped into water the whole surface was evenly wetted and the water did not gather in beads. The clean surface was dipped in a silvering solution which was a solution of silver nitrate specially prepared so that it could be easily reduced to silver. The glass, coated with a thin layer of this solution, was then dipped in sugar solution to reduce the nitrate to silver. Enormous mirrors of this type began to be made.

Henry Draper introduced the silver-on-glass mirror to America, and in 1840, using a mirror system, he succeeded in taking a photograph of the Moon. Photographic attachments to telescopes have now become commonplace.

Aluminium has since been found to be a better reflector of light than silver. In 1934 a piece of glass was given the first successful aluminium coating. The mirror reflected 50% more light than its silver counterpart. This was another step in favour of reflecting telescopes. The largest mirror in existence, in the Hale telescope at Mount Palomar, has a diameter of 200 inches and is coated with aluminium.

CHAPTER THIRTY-ONE

Modern Telescopes

THE CHIEF requirement of a telescope, so far as the average person is concerned, is the ability to magnify small and distant objects. Certainly, the astronomer would not deny that this is extremely desirable, yet the most important function of the instrument in the field of astronomy is simply to gather light. The light of the Sun, Moon and brighter planets reaches us in comparative abundance. But, unfortunately, the celestial bodies about which the astronomer is most curious are situated at such enormous distances from our Solar System that their level of luminosity is thousands of times fainter than that of our Moon.

Telescopes are divided into two broad classes, Refractors (lens telescopes) and Reflectors (mirror telescopes), and with the more recent advent of Maksutov-type instruments the two classes overlap. Reflecting telescopes produce images entirely free from chromatic aberration (the lens defect which produces rainbow fringes around an image) — a decided advantage over the refractor for certain types of work. On the other hand, refractors are free of the diffraction effects which arise from the slight bending of light around the supports of the second mirror in the reflecting telescope, although these effects are not necessarily obtrusive.

Of the two, the refracting telescope is familiar to everyone; the marine spy-glass, binoculars and opera glasses use a principle which is the same as that employed in the astronomers' instruments. This system is

illustrated on page 104. Light from the object under observation enters the objective lens at A. Objective lenses are nearly always corrected for chromatic aberration if employed in astronomical work — there are exceptions, particularly in the field of Solar astronomy, but these are outside the scope of this article. The light is refracted, or bent, by an amount which is determined by the curves of the objective lens, and forms an image at B. This image is inverted, in the same way that an image thrown by a camera lens upon a photographic film or plate is inverted; in fact, if we place a photographic plate at B we simply turn

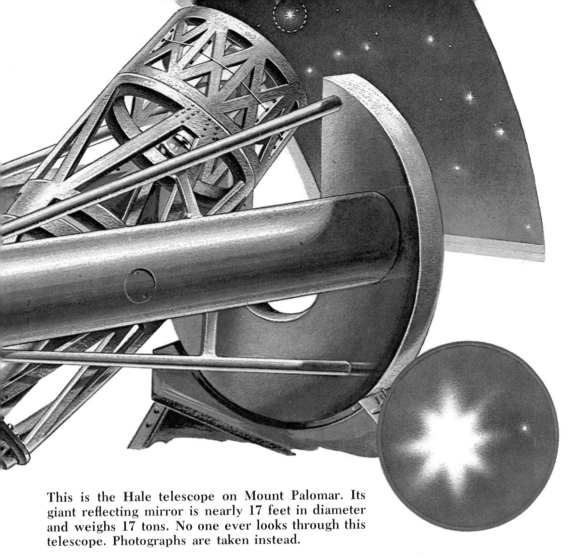

This is the Hale telescope on Mount Palomar. Its giant reflecting mirror is nearly 17 feet in diameter and weighs 17 tons. No one ever looks through this telescope. Photographs are taken instead.

the telescope into a camera, which is precisely what the astronomer does to secure his photographs. The function of the small lens at C is to magnify the image formed by the front lens, and is called the eyepiece. By substituting lenses of different focal lengths the magnifying power of the telescope can be varied.

In this era of giant reflectors it is perhaps surprising to learn that this type of instrument is a comparative latecomer to the field. The actual principle dates back over two hundred years, but the task of adapting the principle satisfactorily received a number of technical setbacks during this time. Today, large telescopes are

invariably reflectors, and it is doubtful whether the forty-inch refractor of Yerkes Observatory at Williams Bay, Wisconsin, will ever be bettered. There are a number of reasons for this. While the casting of large glass discs is still a matter of extraordinary skill and considerable expense, the casting of large discs of optically pure glass suitable for working into lenses is infinitely more difficult than casting mirror-blanks. The thickness of a lens will increase with diameter, and this will mean an increase in the amount of light absorbed in the glass — hardly a situation likely to appeal to the astronomer. Moreover, a lens must be supported at the edge; a massive

103

A *refracting tele-scope.* Objective lens A forms a real image at B which is observed through the magnifying eye-piece C.

Newtonian form of *reflecting telescope.* Real image formed by the concave mir-ror is observed through side of tele-scope.

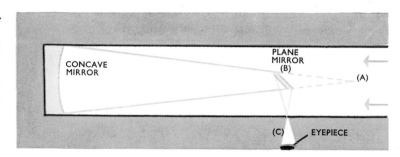

Cassegrain form of *reflecting telescope.* Real image formed by the concave mir-ror is observed through end of tele-scope.

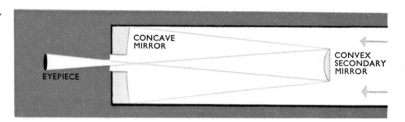

disc of glass (the Yerkes lens weighs 500 lb.) thus supported will be liable to distort under its own weight and this will have an extremely detri-mental effect upon the image.

These problems do not arise with the reflecting telescope. The optical purity of the glass is not necessarily

the most important feature of the mirror, providing that the surface which is to be worked optically fulfils certain requirements. This, of course, is the essential difference between both systems; light passes *through* the lens of a refractor, hence the need of optical purity; it is *reflected* from

The terrestrial telescope.

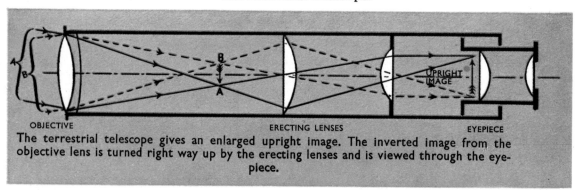

The terrestrial telescope gives an enlarged upright image. The inverted image from the objective lens is turned right way up by the erecting lenses and is viewed through the eye-piece.

the *surface* of the reflector's mirror without being affected by the quality of glass beneath.

The second diagram on page 104 shows the principle of the Newtonian reflector. Light passes along the telescope tube and falls on the surface of the mirror. The mirror surface, shaped very accurately to parabolic form, is coated very thinly with a film of silver or aluminium (present-day mirrors are normally coated with aluminium since silver so readily deteriorates in the presence of atmospheric impurities). The parabolic mirror forms an image at its focal point A. But before the pencil of rays reaches this point it is intercepted by the plane mirror B, inclined at 45° to the optical axis of the primary mirror. The pencil of rays turns to form an image beyond the light-receiving area of the large mirror, where it is magnified by the eye-lens C. This was the development of Sir Isaac Newton, hence the name of this type of system. This type of reflector is favoured by the amateur because of its basic simplicity. However, large modern instruments are not rigidly designed around this principle alone; greater flexibility is obtained by incorporating another optical system, that of Cassegrain.

In the Cassegrain system the small secondary mirror B is replaced by a convex secondary, and a hole is pierced in the primary mirror. The image and eyepiece lie behind the main mirror, a distinct advantage in several ways. Perhaps the greatest advantage of this type of system is that the focal length of a large mirror is folded back, reducing what might otherwise be a long unwieldy telescope tube to an instrument of more manageable proportions.

There is a long-standing dispute regarding the relative merits of refractors and reflectors. Among amateurs, those who possess large telescopes invariably favour reflectors and a high percentage of them are home-made. The production of a small telescope mirror is more a feat of determination and patience than inherent skill, and it only requires an extremely modest initial outlay. The cost of producing a twelve-inch achromatic lens, apart from the labour involved, is so great as to be well-nigh prohibitive, but twelve-inch reflectors are quite common in amateur observatories. Moreover, where garden space is at a premium the usual refractor focal-ratio (focal length ÷ diameter of aperture) of $f15$ compares unfavourably with that of the average reflector, $f6$.

Whether employing refractors or reflectors, the amateur is essentially an observer, drawn to astronomy, simply because it appeals to him, and being free to concentrate on any particular branch at will, he covers an extensive field. Apart from his telescope he needs only a Star Chart, a reasonably accurate watch and clear skies.

Care and accuracy are qualities that cannot be divorced from an observation. The date, time, aperture of instrument used, magnification and clarity of seeing are an essential part of it, and must be entered in the Observation Book as a matter of course. Before an observation is commenced the telescope must be carefully focused by moving the eyepiece towards or away from the lens or mirror. When properly focused, star images should appear as sharp tiny points of light, or if the Moon is being observed, the edge — limb to an

The 60-inch reflecting telescope at Mount Wilson

astronomer — should be crisply defined. Sometimes it will be impossible to focus properly; this will be due to atmospheric tremors, and nothing can be done about that.

A wristwatch is a necessary part of every observer's equipment. It should be checked for accuracy against radio time signals. Every detail entered in the observation book must be accompanied by the time of its appearance. Time can be entered as G.M.T., but a more useful system is G.M.A.T. (Greenwich Mean Astronomical Time). In this system midday is 0 hours G.M.A.T., and midnight 12 hours G.M.A.T. The obvious advantage is that it avoids a change of date during the night. An observation, no matter how carefully conducted, is quite worthless if the time has been omitted. Summer Time, incidentally, is not used in astronomy.

Not all observations are made in the form of notes or timechecks. Drawings of the planets are always interesting, and sometimes valuable. They should be neatly made and contain only those details the observer has seen with *absolute certainty*. 'Artistic Licence' has no place in astronomical drawings. In fact, it is not even necessary for an observer to possess any particular talent with a pencil, so long as he is satisfied that his drawing contains all the details he saw in their correct positions. He should gain heart from the knowledge that his drawing, made with modest equipment, will almost certainly show as much detail as a photograph made with an instrument several times larger. Finally, each drawing should be accompanied by the date, time, magnification, state of seeing (good, bad, or any relevant remarks) and the observer's name.

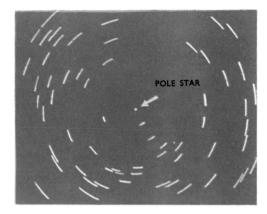

Because of Earth's rotation, stars *appear to move* during observation. Long exposure photograph *(above)* shows them as streaks (except for Pole Star which is virtually in line with Earth's axis).

The amateur will soon discover that few nights allow first-class observing. A dark winter's night, with the stars flashing like gems against the velvet sky, will almost certainly be disappointing, because the fact that the stars flash and tremble at all denotes an unsteady, turbulent atmosphere. On the other hand, misty nights are frequently nights of clear seeing — at least, for the planets; the fainter stars will be almost blotted out on such an evening. Some experience is needed to judge the state of the atmosphere before actually observing; until this is gained the beginner should attempt to observe on every clear night.

Limited only by the extent and quality of whatever equipment he is able to obtain for himself, or share with others, the amateur enjoys a freedom which the professional astronomer might well envy. Historically the amateur has played a significant part in the sphere of discovery, particularly in the fields of lunar and planetary observation, although, alas, few can hope to fill this role today.

Yet to recognise, and work within his limitations is the hallmark of the serious amateur, as the highly interesting and ingenious papers regularly published in the various astronomical journals so clearly demonstrate.

An excellent example of valuable amateur work is the vast number of variable star observations annually collected at Harvard Observatory for analysis by the professional astronomer, a type of observation admirably suited to small telescopes, and a singularly useful liaison for the professional, since it releases him from the more onerous business of routine observations.

An astronomical telescope is fitted with a smaller low-power telescope near the eyepiece, called a Finder. Without the aid of a finder it is often very difficult to bring the main telescope to bear upon the desired object, owing to its narrow field of view.

FINDER

CHAPTER THIRTY-TWO

Radio Astronomy

WHEN A STAR explodes to form a supernova, it radiates an enormous amount of light energy. The atoms of the stars are suddenly given a great amount of energy; they become very hot, and, in common with all very hot bodies, they radiate much of the energy as light waves. The star appears much brighter. Besides visible light, the star emits other kinds of radiation — invisible infra-red rays, ultra-violet rays and radio waves. All these types of radiation become much more intense at the time of a supernova. Radio Astronomy is concerned with the last of these, the *radio waves*.

The force of the explosion accelerates clouds of electrically charged particles away from the star. Associated with them are turbulent, rapidly changing magnetic fields.

Whenever charged particles move through magnetic fields, they gain energy, and they radiate the energy as *electromagnetic waves*. One of the common waves emitted by charged atoms of hydrogen has a wavelength of 21 centimetres.

Electromagnetic waves of this wavelength are *radio waves*. They spread out from their source in all directions, and they travel with the speed of light. (Light waves are also a kind of electromagnetic radiation, but of much shorter wavelength.)

Radio waves are emitted by all galaxies and many stars, including the Sun. The Sun is not a very 'bright' radio star, but during periods of sunspot activity its radio wave emission increases. 'Bright' sources of radio waves do not necessarily coincide with visually bright objects, like stars.

In fact, radio waves come from black regions of the sky, dark clouds of dust and hydrogen gas, where the hydrogen atoms are in the process of concentrating together to form new stars. They radiate the energy gained by accelerating in magnetic fields in space.

Radio waves are invisible, and they cannot be detected with optical telescopes. But, like any radio broadcast, they can be picked up by a receiving aerial. The waves induce minute electric currents to flow up and down the aerial.

A large single reflecting radio 'mirror', which can be steered to point at any area of the sky.

The 60-ft. reflecting radio telescope at Harvard Observatory, U.S.A.

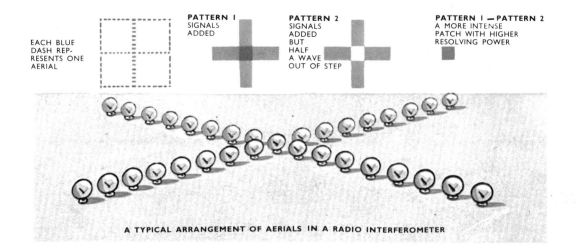

EACH BLUE DASH REPRESENTS ONE AERIAL

PATTERN I
SIGNALS
ADDED

PATTERN 2
SIGNALS
ADDED
BUT
HALF
A WAVE
OUT OF STEP

PATTERN I — PATTERN 2
A MORE INTENSE
PATCH WITH HIGHER
RESOLVING POWER

A TYPICAL ARRANGEMENT OF AERIALS IN A RADIO INTERFEROMETER

The currents can be amplified, sorted out and turned into audible sounds, as in an ordinary radio receiver. But it is more usual to use a specially designed receiver to pick up radio waves from space. Then the fluctuating currents from the aerial are automatically recorded on a graph. As well as this, they may be fed straight into an electronic computer for analysis.

Radio telescopes are large aerials designed to intercept as much of the radio emission from a star or galaxy as possible. Then the waves are gathered up together and concentrated so that the fluctuating currents they produce in the aerial are big enough to be detected.

The radio waves spread out from their sources in all directions. Only a tiny fraction of the total radiation from a star is intercepted by the Earth, and the radiation has travelled over such vast distances that the waves are virtually parallel to each other. The radio telescope picks up the parallel beams from one source over as wide an area as possible, and then concentrates them by focusing them onto the aerial. The bigger the area, the more sensitive the telescope, as more of the radio waves from a distant star are collected.

The biggest optical telescopes are huge paraboloidal mirror reflectors. Rays striking the bowl of the paraboloidal mirror are all reflected onto a small mirror at its focus. They can then be reflected by this small mirror to strike a photographic film. The large paraboloidal mirror collects all the light rays falling over a wide area.

Some large radio telescopes are very similar to this. The radio 'mirror' is also a paraboloid and it may be several hundred feet in diameter. The smaller mirror at the focus of an optical telescope is replaced in the radio telescope by the aerial and all the waves are focused onto it.

But there is one serious drawback with radio telescopes. Even though there may be three or four separate sources of radio waves in the field of view, it is impossible to distinguish between them. The fluctuating currents are the result of *all* the radio waves received over *all* the field of view of the telescope. The photographic plate in an optical telescope is a much better means of detecting the picture. Rays of light striking the

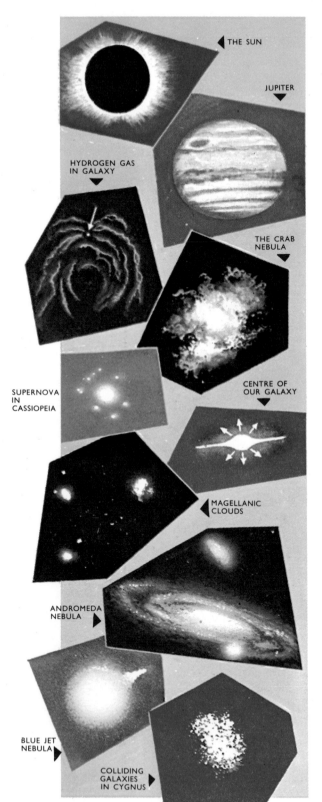

THE SUN

JUPITER

HYDROGEN GAS
IN GALAXY

THE CRAB
NEBULA

SUPERNOVA
IN
CASSIOPEIA

CENTRE OF
OUR GALAXY

MAGELLANIC
CLOUDS

ANDROMEDA
NEBULA

BLUE JET
NEBULA

COLLIDING
GALAXIES
IN CYGNUS

The Radio Sky—some 'bright' Radio Sources

Radio Source	Time radio waves have taken to travel to Earth	Prominent wavelengths
Sun	8 minutes	Several millimetres to several metres, emitted by corona and chromosphere
Jupiter	40 minutes	About 15 metres
Hydrogen gas in spiral arms of galaxy	1,500-80,000 years	21.1 centimetres emitted by ionized hydrogen gas
Crab Nebula (supernova)	3,000 years	1 centimetre to 10 metres. Waves from accelerated electrons
Supernova in Cassiopeia	10,000 years	1 centimetre to 10 metres—from ionized hydrogen, oxygen and neon gas
Centre of galaxy	30,000 years	
Magellanic Clouds (the nearest galaxies)	200,000 years	21.1 centimetres
Andromeda nebula (the nearest spiral galaxy)	2 million years	21.1 centimetres—about as powerful a radio emitter as our own galaxy
Elliptical galaxy in Virgo (Virgo A)—the blue jet nebula	33 million years	Waves from accelerated electrons
Two colliding spiral galaxies in Cygnus (Cygnus A)	50 million years	
Distant radio nebula in Hercules	750 million years	

mirror at different angles are concentrated on slightly different points on the small mirror, and then reflected to blacken different points on the sensitive plate.

The ideal radio telescope should be as large as possible to collect as many rays as possible, but it should also be manoeuvrable, so that it can be pointed at any area of the sky. When the diameter is greater than about 250 feet, the telescope cannot be made rigid enough to withstand winds without bending and distorting the 'picture'. It also becomes difficult to move the telescope. A radio telescope with a diameter of 1,000 feet has been built in Puerto Rico by lining the walls of a conveniently-shaped crater with polished aluminium. But the telescope cannot be moved.

Large single reflecting radio telescopes are difficult and expensive to construct. A different kind of radio telescope is made up of several smaller reflectors and aerials. These are pointed at different areas of the sky, and they are moved, relative to each other, so covering a larger area than a much bigger single reflector could. The radio 'picture' can then be pieced together from fragments in different portions.

Long ranks of identical reflectors and aerials, arranged exactly the same distance apart, are used to pin-point bright radio sources more accurately. They are better at separating two nearby sources of waves. Although all the rays from one point source are parallel, if they strike the telescope at an angle, they will hit the aerial at one end of the line before they hit the aerial at the other end of the line. Because the waves have hit the aerials at different times, the waves at each end will be at a different stage of their up and down, crest and trough vibration.

When all the currents from all the aerials are added up, those at one end may be flowing in the opposite direction to those at the other end. They partially cancel each other out, the effect of this being to sharpen the radio image of the star. This kind of radio telescope is called a *radio interferometer*, since the cancelling out of one set of waves with another set of waves is called *interference*. The radio interferometer usually consists of two banks of aerials at right-angles to each other. The sharpness of the image, or *resolving power,* can be increased in various ways, by adding and subtracting signals from the different aerials.

Radio telescopes can penetrate much deeper into the Universe than optical telescopes. The most distant galaxies known are also the most powerful radio transmitters — they were discovered by this powerful radio emission, probably emitted because they are colliding galaxies. The 200-inch optical telescope at Mount Palomar afterwards searched extensively in this direction, and found the faint cluster of galaxies causing the radio waves.

The Earth's atmosphere is a nuisance in radio astronomy, since it absorbs a large proportion of the electromagnetic radiation reaching the Earth. Only a narrow range of radio waves can penetrate the atmosphere. Short wavelength radio waves are absorbed by atmospheric molecules, and long wavelength rays are distorted by electrically-charged layers of particles in the ionosphere.

Putting the radio telescope on an artificial satellite is one answer. A more promising idea is to build a radio telescope on the Moon, which has no atmosphere to interrupt the radiation. Larger telescopes could be assembled on the Moon, as the gravitational force there is less, and the structure could be steered with less effort and less distortion of the reflector.

CHAPTER THIRTY-THREE

Döppler Effect—the Red Shift

LIGHT WAVES are altered if either the source emitting them or the observer is moving. This is one of the many unusual effects which happen because light is a kind of wave motion, and it is known as the *Döppler effect*.

The same effect is easily noticeable where sound waves are concerned. To a listener by the side of a racetrack, the sound of a car changes as it flashes past. When the car is moving away from him, the pitch, or *frequency* of the sound it makes appears to be lower than when it was approaching him. The frequency of the sound is the number of waves emitted in one second. As the car approaches, this number of waves is 'compressed' into a shorter distance; more waves reach the ear of the listener each second, and he hears a sound of higher frequency. As the car moves away, the sound waves are 'stretched out' and their frequency appears to be lower.

With sound waves, the Döppler effect brings about a change in frequency. The same happens with light waves, but the frequency change means a change in colour. Light of high frequency (and short wavelength) gives the colour sensation we know as blue, while light of low frequency (and long wavelength) appears to us as red. When a source of light is moving towards an observer, the increase in frequency means that the observer sees a slightly bluer light; when it is moving away from an observer the frequency is decreased, and the light appears redder.

Two prominent dark lines crossing the spectra of light from distant galaxies show that calcium in the atmosphere of the stars has absorbed certain frequencies. These lines are 'shifted' towards the red end of the spectrum. This red shift can be interpreted as a Döppler effect and means that the galaxies must be receding from the Earth at fantastic speeds. The more distant the galaxy, the bigger the red shift.

NEBULA IN VIRGO— 20,000,000 LIGHT YEARS AWAY

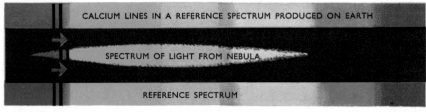

CALCIUM LINES IN A REFERENCE SPECTRUM PRODUCED ON EARTH

SPECTRUM OF LIGHT FROM NEBULA

REFERENCE SPECTRUM

ABOVE: AMOUNT OF RED SHIFT IMPLIES THAT NEBULA IS MOVING AT 750 MILES PER SECOND

BELOW: BIGGER RED SHIFT. NEBULA IS MOVING AT 9,300 MILES PER SECOND

NEBULA IN URSA MAJOR 300,000,000 LIGHT YEARS AWAY

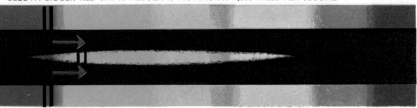

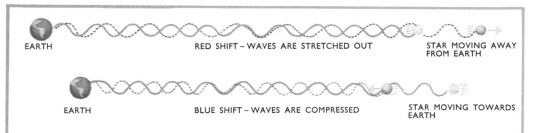

EARTH   RED SHIFT – WAVES ARE STRETCHED OUT   STAR MOVING AWAY FROM EARTH

EARTH   BLUE SHIFT – WAVES ARE COMPRESSED   STAR MOVING TOWARDS EARTH

The 'red shift' in light from a distant star is thought to be due to the Döppler effect. If the star is moving away from the Earth, its light waves are 'stretched out'. Their apparent wavelength is longer (and of course their frequency is lower). Hence the light appears redder. If the star moves towards the Earth, light waves are 'compressed' and appear bluer.

Changes in light frequency can be observed only by examining the light with a spectroscope, an instrument which splits it up into its different colours. A narrow slit of light is allowed to pass through the instrument, and the images of this slit are focused as 'spectral lines' on a screen. If the light from a sodium lamp is examined in this way, its spectrum is seen to consist of two bright yellow lines close to each other. If the sodium lamp were moving fast enough away from the observer, the yellow lines would be shifted slightly towards the red end of the spectrum, and the colour would become more orange.

If, on the other hand, it were moving towards the observer, the lines would move towards the blue end of the spectrum, and so would be tinged with green.

This *red shift* or *blue shift* is observable only if the source of light is moving at a speed which is an appreciable fraction of the speed of light — 186,000 miles per second. It was first noted in the spectra of light reaching the Earth from distant stars and galaxies. The kind of light emitted by stars and other very hot bodies does not consist of light of definite frequencies, as does sodium light, but consists of a *continuous* range of frequen-

NEBULA IN BOOTES – 800,000,000 LIGHT YEARS AWAY

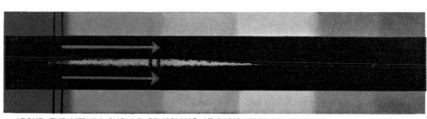

ABOVE: THE NEBULA SHOULD BE MOVING AT 24,000 MILES PER SECOND

BELOW : THE NEBULA IS MOVING AT ABOUT 38,000 MILES PER SECOND

NEBULA IN HYDRA – 1,200,000,000 LIGHT YEARS AWAY

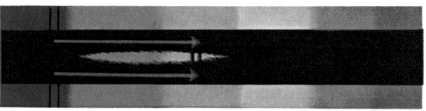

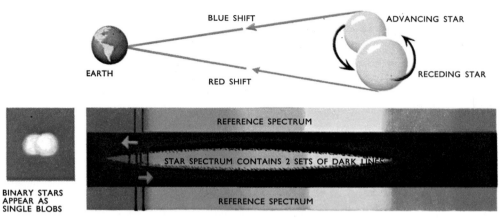

Light from what appears to be a single star contains two definite sets of spectral lines. So there must be *two* stars, revolving around each other.

cies. However, in passing through the outer, cooler layers of the star's atmosphere, some of the light is absorbed. Certain elements present in the star's atmosphere have the property of absorbing certain frequencies of light. So these frequencies are missing from the light reaching the Earth. A careful examination of the spectra of stars shows that the continuous spectrum (from violet to red) is crossed by a number of dark lines, called *Fraunhofer lines*. The lines can be identified with the same lines produced under similar conditions on Earth. (Since each line corresponds to an element, an examination of the spectrum tells astronomers which elements are present in the atmosphere of the star.)

But dark lines in the spectra from very distant stars and galaxies show a pronounced shift towards the red end of the spectrum. The most prominent dark lines are those due to the element calcium. On the Earth (*i.e.* when there is no movement between source and observer) these lines can be seen only faintly in the far violet end of the spectrum. In some very distant stars examined by

this method, these lines have shifted half-way across the visible spectrum into the green. All stars and galaxies of stars show, to some degree, this red shift. It can be interpreted as meaning that they are all actually receding away from the Earth, and the more distant the galaxy, the more quickly it appears to be receding. In fact, there is a very definite relationship between the distance of the star (as checked by other astronomical methods) and the speed of recession, as measured by the red shift. In most cases the red shift is the only method of calculating how far the galaxy in question is away from the Earth.

The Döppler effect can also be used to distinguish binary systems, two stars which revolve around each other, sometimes so close that they appear as one through a telescope. The spectrum of what appears to be a single source of light contains *two* definite sets of dark lines, one due to each star. And since at any instant one of the revolving pair may be moving towards the Earth while the other moves away, one set of lines shows a red shift while the other shows a blue shift.

CHAPTER THIRTY-FOUR

Measuring the Extent of the Universe

A RADIO TELESCOPE picks up a faint signal from a remote, unknown object in the sky. Then photographs of this area are taken with optical telescopes. A faint blur on the photograph is investigated. The spectrum of the star is analysed, and the light is adjudged to come from a galaxy 5,000,000,000 light years away. This galaxy, in the constellation of Boötes, is the most distant galaxy to be seen with a telescope. At present, it marks the limit of the observable Universe.

How can astronomers be certain that this distance is accurate? The answer is that they cannot. Their estimate may be a thousand million light years out, but at least it is thought to be of the right order of magnitude.

Distance-measuring in astronomy is a very tricky business. First, distances measured between two points on Earth must be accurate. Distances on Earth are used as a basis for measuring longer distances. Each time a big distance can be found accurately, it becomes the basis for measuring even bigger distances.

Often the methods are very roundabout, for distances cannot be measured directly. They are estimated by measuring some of the properties of the light from the star, which depend indirectly on distance.

Triangles in Proportion

The basis of all distance-measurement is a standard unit of length — in scientific circles, the metre. And the most important construction is the *triangle,* for until recently, the triangle was used for all surveying and distance measuring on the Earth itself.

The surveyor knows, for instance, that if he constructs a triangle with its base one metre long, and its other

This triangle is drawn on a scale measurable with a metre rule. Once short distances are known accurately, longer distances can be measured from them.

The whole Earth can be charted by successive triangulation. Long distances on Earth are used as the basis of triangulating the Moon and the planets.

The triangle below has a base 1,000 metres long. If large-scale triangles have the same angles as small-scale triangles, the lengths of their sides are all in proportion.

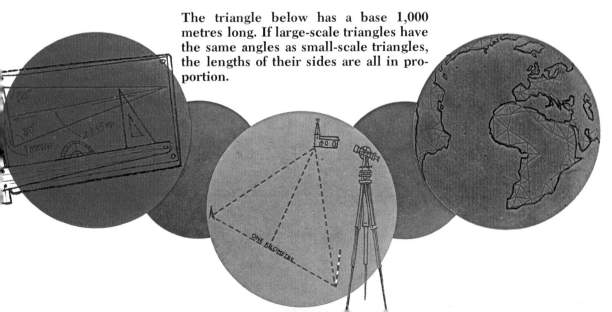

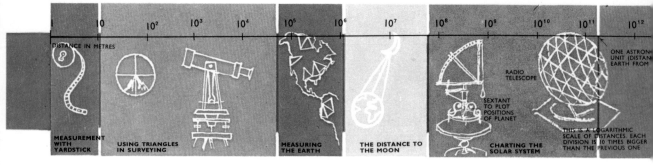

DISTANCE IN METRES

MEASUREMENT WITH YARDSTICK

USING TRIANGLES IN SURVEYING

MEASURING THE EARTH

THE DISTANCE TO THE MOON

RADIO TELESCOPE

SEXTANT TO PLOT POSITIONS OF PLANET

CHARTING THE SOLAR SYSTEM

THIS IS A LOGARITHMIC SCALE OF DISTANCES. EACH DIVISION IS 10 TIMES BIGGER THAN THE PREVIOUS ONE

ONE ASTRONO UNIT (DISTAN EARTH FROM

two sides making an angle of 80° with the base, he can measure anything there is to measure about the triangle. An important length is the distance from the point where the two sloping sides meet to the centre of the base. This is 2·835 metres long.

He then uses a similar triangle. For example, his new base may be 1,000 metres long, accurately measured along the surface of the Earth. He observes a prominent object nearby and measures the angle his line of sight makes with the base-line. If the angle at both ends is 80°, he knows for certain that the triangles are *similar*, and that the object is 2,285 metres away from the centre of his base-line. The angles of the large-scale triangle are exactly the same as the angles in the small-scale triangle, and all lengths associated with the triangle are increased in proportion. The whole Earth can be charted by successive *triangulation*.

The first step into space is the triangulation of the Moon. The Moon is observed at the same time from the two ends of a long base-line on Earth. It seems to occupy slightly different positions against the 'fixed' starry background. The apparent position is

By carefully plotting their movements, and knowing the laws of motion of the planets, a scale model of the Solar System could be made.

When observed at the same time from two different points on the Earth, the Moon's position is different. Its distance is calculated from the parallax shift.

One accurately measured distance in the Solar System gives the scale of the whole system. This is found by bouncing radar waves off Venus.

MOON SEEN AGAINST 'FIXED' BACKGROUND OF STARS

PARALLAX SHIFT

AN OLD-FASHIONED SEXTANT FOR PLOTTING POSITIONS OF PLANETS

SCALE MODEL OF THE SOLAR SYSTEM

RADIO-TELESCOPE ON EARTH

RADAR BEAM

REFLECTED BEAM

EARTH'S ORBIT

VENUS' ORBIT

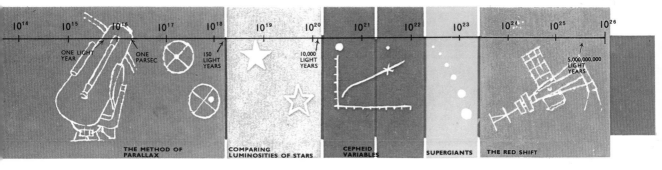

10^{14} 10^{15} 10^{16} 10^{17} 10^{18} 10^{19} 10^{20} 10^{21} 10^{22} 10^{23} 10^{24} 10^{25} 10^{26}

ONE LIGHT YEAR   ONE PARSEC   150 LIGHT YEARS   10,000 LIGHT YEARS   5,000,000,000 LIGHT YEARS

THE METHOD OF PARALLAX   COMPARING LUMINOSITIES OF STARS   CEPHEID VARIABLES   SUPERGIANTS   THE RED SHIFT

measured. From the angles, the distance of the Moon can be calculated. This is called the *method of parallax*.

Radar and Scale Models

The next important distance to be measured is the distance of the Earth from the Sun. This distance is given the special name *the astronomical unit*. It is, however, impossible to measure the shift in the angular position of the Sun at the two different ends of a base-line, because the brightness of the Sun blocks out the starry background. An indirect method is called for. The movement of the planets is charted. They follow elliptical orbits around the Sun. The periods of their orbits and their speeds depend on their distances from the Sun. In fact, from their observations astronomers could make a scale model of the Solar System. All the planetary orbits are in the right proportion. Discover any one of the distances absolutely and the right scale of the Solar System immediately follows.

The most accurate distance known in the Solar System is the distance between the Earth and Venus. It has been determined by bouncing radar signals off Venus. Radar waves travel with the speed of light, which is known accurately. The time between the sending of the radar beam and reception of the radar 'echo' is measured. Knowing this and the speed of the radar waves it is a simple matter to calculate the distance of the planet.

With the diameter of the Earth's orbit as a base, the parallax of nearby stars is found. Parallax becomes negligible beyond distances of 150 light years.

The period and the luminosity of the Cepheid variable stars obey a known rule. The luminosity of a distant Cepheid follows once its period is known.

The photograph reveals the apparent luminosity of the stars. The spectra show that they are of the same type. It also shows the real difference in luminosity.

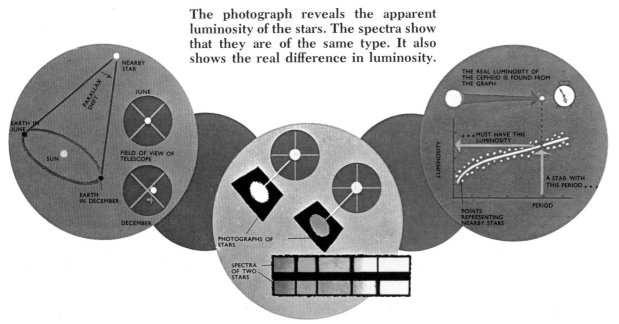

The scale of the whole Solar System is found and with it an accurate measurement of the astronomical unit. The mean distance of Earth from the Sun is 92,960,000 miles.

Parallax and the Parsec

The diameter of the Earth's elliptical orbit makes a very useful baseline for triangulation and the method of parallax. Again, the idea is to measure the shift in position of a nearby star against the background of 'fixed' stars—(these are much farther away, so hardly appear to shift at all). The positions are charted at time intervals of 6 months when the Earth is at opposite ends of its orbit. This must be done very accurately, because the parallax angles are very small indeed —the biggest one is less than an (angular) second (*i.e.* less than a 360th of a degree).

At this distance the mile becomes a small unit. It is replaced by two much larger units—the *parsec,* the distance at which the parallax angle is one

second, and the *light year,* the distance light travels in one year (5,880,000,000,000 miles). One parsec is 3·26 light years. The light year is the more convenient unit and it is used right to the limit of the observable Universe.

Comparing Luminosities

Parallax is no use for distances greater than 150 light years. The parallax angle is masked by other effects, and is too small to be measured accurately. The method which replaces it can work because there are a very large number of stars in the sky. Stars fall into different types—*spectral types.* The spectrum of the light from the star shows which colours of light are given out by the star in their *relative proportions.* If two stars give out exactly the same relative proportions of all the different colours, it is reasonable to suppose that they are the same type of star. Probably they are of the same luminosity, and roughly the same size.

All supergiants, the largest of stars, are assumed to have the same absolute luminosity. By finding their apparent luminosity, distance can be found.

The distance of a whole cluster of stars is found by measuring the distance of a single Cepheid variable star in the cluster.

All the distant galaxies are receding away from the Earth. Their speed is a measure of their distance, and can be calculated from the red shift.

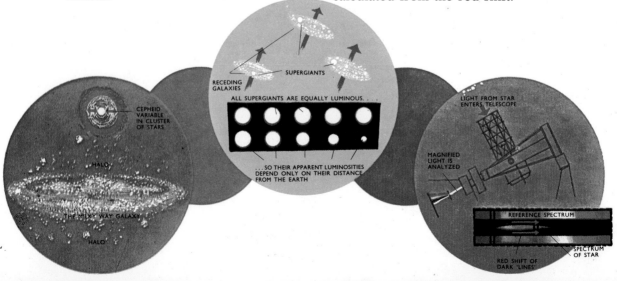

Two stars are giving out the same amount of light. The distance of the nearer one is measured by parallax. But because its light has travelled a shorter distance, its light appears more intense. The distance of the second star can be calculated since it is known exactly by how much the extra faintness results from the extra distance travelled by light.

This works up to distances of 10,000 light years, and it covers only a very small fraction of our own galaxy. Beyond this, other effects distort the spectral lines and the method is no longer accurate enough. Next comes the Cepheid variable, the star whose luminosity changes regularly.

The Cepheid Variables

The previous method compared the *luminosities* of stars. Their distances can then be compared by assuming that the stars are really of the same luminosity. When Cepheid variables are used, the luminosities are also compared but with the extra assumption that the Cepheid is behaving in a regular way. Its light brightens and fades at regular intervals of time. The luminosity can be calculated from the period because luminosity and period of Cepheid variables vary according to a known rule.

The nearby Cepheids are charted and their distances measured. This enables their (average) luminosity to be worked out. Then it is assumed that the period luminosity rule applies to distant Cepheids in the same way as nearer Cepheids. A distant Cepheid has a certain period so it must have a certain luminosity. Luminosities are compared, and the distance found.

Often Cepheids, which are all very bright stars, can easily be distinguished from clusters of stars.

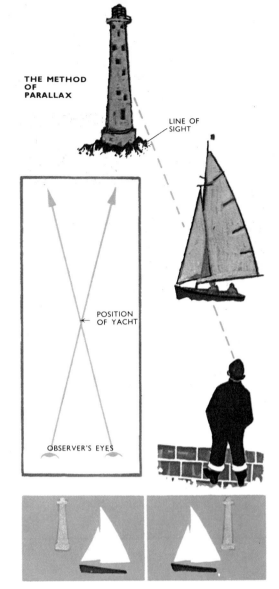

THE METHOD OF PARALLAX

LINE OF SIGHT

POSITION OF YACHT

OBSERVER'S EYES

The left-eye view differs from the right-eye view, because of parallax. The distance between the observer's eyes is the base of the triangle. The observer can work out, roughly, the distance of the yacht.

About 3% of all visible stars are Cepheids, so it is reasonable to suppose that there will be some observable ones in star clusters containing up to a million stars. Many stars tend to form in clusters. One Cepheid in one cluster is used to measure the distance of the whole group. All the stars are at roughly the same distance.

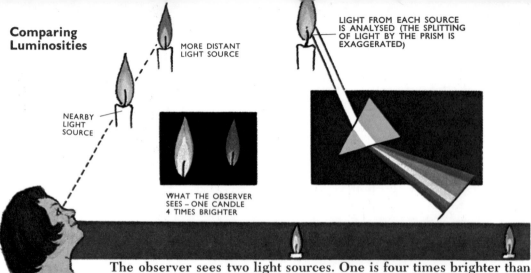

Comparing Luminosities

MORE DISTANT LIGHT SOURCE

NEARBY LIGHT SOURCE

LIGHT FROM EACH SOURCE IS ANALYSED (THE SPLITTING OF LIGHT BY THE PRISM IS EXAGGERATED)

WHAT THE OBSERVER SEES – ONE CANDLE 4 TIMES BRIGHTER

The observer sees two light sources. One is four times brighter than the other. Light from both has similar spectra and it is assumed that they come from similar sources. Light intensity falls off according to an *inverse square law*, so the observer works out that one candle is twice as far away as the other.

The Supergiants

After the Cepheids become too faint to be seen, the next useful stars are the supergiants, the brightest of all stars. The assumption made is that all the supergiants everywhere are of the same brightness. This is thought to be a fair assumption, since there seems to be a limit on the size and brightness of stars. The supergiants are the only stars distinguishable from the rest of the galaxies. So, again, by comparing their luminosities with nearer supergiants, their distances can be worked out. Galaxies occur in clusters. From one prominent supergiant in one galaxy the distance of all the millions of millions of stars in the galaxy cluster is estimated.

The Red Shift

When even supergiants are no longer prominent in the galaxy, the light from the whole galaxy is examined. It is split into its spectrum. Distinguishing features in the spectrum are prominent dark lines caused by absorption of light by the galaxy. These dark lines normally occur at the very far end of the blue end of the spectrum. But if the galaxy is moving quickly away from the Earth, (as galaxies invariably are), the light waves are distorted.

Their wavelength increases, because light waves are 'pulled out' and stretched as the galaxy moves away. An increase in wavelength implies a shift towards the red end (longer wavelength) of the visible spectrum. The shift is only small when the velocity is small. When the velocity is much bigger, the shift is much bigger. This is called the *red shift*.

With the nearer stars, observations have shown that the more distant the stars are, the bigger the shift to the red part of the spectrum. More distant stars seem to be speeding more quickly away from the Earth. Distant stars are rapidly becoming more distant.

In the light received from the galaxy in Boötes the lines are shifted red-endwards for over half the width of the visible spectrum. The shift shows that the velocity of the galaxy is 90,000 miles per second. Providing that the shift increases with distance, this corresponds to a distance of 5,000,000,000,000 light years.

Glossary of Terms

Aberration. The very slight movement in the apparent position of a star, caused by the rotation of the Earth, between the time light from the star reaches the objective of the telescope and the time it reaches the eyepiece.

Absorption. The stopping and reduction of light by particles of matter it encounters on its path.

Absorption lines. Atoms of each element may absorb light of particular colours, or wavelengths. When the light from a star is split up into its colours, or *wavelengths,* the spectrum is crossed by lines where that particular wavelength has been absorbed.

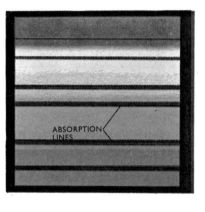

ABSORPTION LINES

Albedo. Bodies like planets emit no light of their own. Their albedo is the ratio of the light they reflect to the light they receive from the Sun.

Altitude. One of the co-ordinates used in locating objects in the sky. It is the angular distance of the object above the horizontal.

Aphelion. The point in the elliptical orbit of a planet, comet or asteroid at which it is at its greatest possible distance from the Sun.

Apogee. The point of the Moon's orbit when it is farthest away from the Earth. The term also applies to artificial satellites.

Asteroids. Lumps of matter between 1 mile and 440 miles across, whose orbits round the Sun lie mainly between Mars and Jupiter.

Astrolabe. An instrument used to measure the angular distance between two stars.

Astronomical Unit. A unit of distance in astronomy. It is the mean distance of the Earth from the Sun (92,960,000 miles).

Atmosphere. The envelope of gases surrounding a heavenly body, held to it by gravitational forces.

Aurora. Displays of light caused by energetic radiation from the Sun, exciting gases in the upper atmosphere.

Azimuth. A co-ordinate used in locating heavenly bodies.

Binary Stars. A pair of stars which revolve about each other. About 50% of all stars are grouped in binaries.

Bode's Law. A rule for working out the distance of the planets from the Sun. It has no scientific basis at all.

Celestial sphere. An imaginary sphere used to locate points in the sky. The observer himself is at the centre of the sphere.

Cepheid Variables. Stars which regularly appear brighter and fainter. They are used to determine distances of stars.

Chromosphere. Part of the Sun's atmosphere between the photosphere (the light-emitting part) and the corona.

Colour Index. A measure of the colour of a star. It is the difference between the observable brightness and the brightness recorded on a photograph which is sensitive to different light wavelengths from the eye.

Comet. A lump of matter which orbits the Sun in an elliptical, parabolic or hyperbolic orbit. A 'tail' of gas is driven out of it when it is near the Sun.

Conjunction. The points in an orbit when a heavenly body is *apparently* close to another heavenly body. Then both are in the same line of sight, as seen from the Earth.

Constellations. The divisions of the stars into groups, used chiefly for identifying particular areas of the celestial sphere. There are 88 of them.

Co-ordinates. The co-ordinates of any point are its distances from fixed, reference *axes,* usually at right angles to each other. The co-ordinates may be the perpendicular distances from the reference axes, or they may be the angular distances (i.e. the angle between the reference axis and the line) from the point of intersection of the reference axes (called the origin) to the point in question.

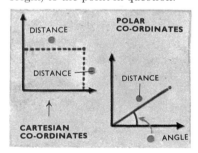

DISTANCE DISTANCE CARTESIAN CO-ORDINATES POLAR CO-ORDINATES DISTANCE ANGLE

Corona. The outermost layer of the Sun's atmosphere, visible only during an eclipse of the Sun.

Cosmic Rays. Very energetic particles which are continually reaching the Earth from outer space. The atmosphere absorbs most of them. Some come from the

Sun, but many are thought to originate outside the Solar System.

Craters. One name for the 'walled plains' of the Moon.

Dark Nebulae. Clouds of dust and gas which obscure the space behind them. They occur mainly in the 'discs' of spiral galaxies, and new stars are thought to be 'born' in them.

Declination. A co-ordinate used in locating stars.

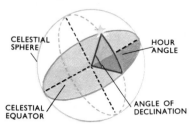

CELESTIAL SPHERE
HOUR ANGLE
CELESTIAL EQUATOR
ANGLE OF DECLINATION

Döppler Effect. An effect which leads to the lengthening of the wavelength of light from a star which is moving away from us. The light then appears redder (the *red shift*).

Dwarf Stars. Tiny, faint stars. The majority of stars in the universe may be dwarfs, but many may be too small to be detected.

Eccentricity. A mathematical term for defining the shape of an orbit. A circular orbit has an eccentricity of 0 (the Earth's orbit is very nearly circular—its eccentricity is 0.017). Orbits with eccentricities between 0 and 1 are ellipses, and those with eccentricities greater than 1 are hyperbolae.

Eclipse. An occasion when one heavenly body passes in front of another and obliterates it.

Ecliptic. The Sun's apparent yearly path on the celestial sphere.

Emission Lines. Bright 'lines' seen in the spectrum of a hot gas. They are formed when individual atoms emit particular wavelengths of light.

Equatorial Mounting. A way of mounting an astronomical telescope, so that it need be rotated about only one axis to follow

exactly the movement of the stars (caused by the Earth's rotation).

Expanding Universe. A theory in which the whole of the universe is slowly expanding.

Extragalactic Nebulae. Galaxies outside our own galaxy (the Milky Way).

Finder Telescope. A small telescope capable of covering a large area of sky. It is attached to a larger telescope and used to position the latter.

Flare. An explosion in the Sun's chromosphere.

Fraunhofer Lines. Absorption lines in the Sun's spectrum.

Galactic Nebulae. Clouds of gas and dust in the spiral disc of the Milky Way.

Galaxy. A huge cluster of stars and other heavenly bodies.

TYPES OF GALAXY

Giant Stars. Huge, bright stars, many of which are expanding.

Globular Cluster. A spherical cluster of up to a million individual older stars. They are found in the halo of the Milky Way.

Granulation. The 'patchiness' of the Sun's disc, caused by 'boiling over' of the gases of the photosphere.

Green Flash. A flash apparently emitted by the setting sun. It is actually caused by refraction of light in the Earth's atmosphere.

Halo. The spherical cloud of older stars surrounding the rest of

the Milky Way.

Hertzsprung-Russell Diagram. A kind of graph on which each star is represented by a speck. The absolute magnitude of the star is plotted on one axis, and the colour on the other. It is useful in classifying stars according to their ages.

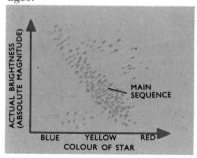

ACTUAL BRIGHTNESS (ABSOLUTE MAGNITUDE)
MAIN SEQUENCE
BLUE   YELLOW   RED
COLOUR OF STAR

Horizon. One of the reference axes in a system of astronomical co-ordinates.

Hour Angle. A co-ordinate used in locating positions in the sky (*see declination*).

Inferior Planet. A planet nearer the Sun than the Earth, i.e. Venus and Mercury.

Intergalactic Matter. Odd bits of matter in the space between galaxies.

Jupiter. The largest planet of the Solar System.

Kepler's Laws. 1. The orbits of the planets are elliptical, with the Sun at one focus. 2. A line drawn from a planet to the Sun sweeps out equal areas in equal times. 3. The length of time taken by a planet to complete its orbit increases the further away it is from the Sun.

Latitude and Longitude. Two co-ordinates used in the *ecliptic system* of locating positions in the sky.

Libration. A to-and-fro and side-to-side movement associated with the Moon's rotation on its axis.

Light-Year. The distance light travels in one year. A distance unit used in measuring distances of stars. One light-year is 5,880,000,000,000 miles.

Lunar Eclipse. Eclipse of the Moon. It occurs when the Moon enters the shadow cast by the Earth.

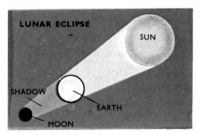

Magellanic Clouds. The nearest galaxies to our own. They are visible only in the Southern Hemisphere. These two galaxies are thought to form a triple system with our galaxy.

Magnitude. The apparent magnitude of a star is a measure of its brightness as seen from the Earth. Bright stars are said to be of the first magnitude, while the faintest star visible to the naked eye has a magnitude of about 6. On this scale brighter stars, such as the Sun, have a negative magnitude. Sirius has a magnitude of −1.6, while the Sun's apparent magnitude is −26.8.

Main Sequence. When stars are grouped on a Hertzsprung-Russell diagram, it is found that the majority of them are positioned along a diagonal line—called the main sequence. The main sequence corresponds to the 'middle age' of stars.

Mars. The planet which occupies the next orbit of the Sun after the Earth. It is the only planet thought to be capable of supporting life (apart from Earth).

Mercury. The innermost planet of the Solar System.

Meteorites. Meteors which reach the Earth's surface before they are completely burnt out by frictional heat.

Meteors. Particles of matter orbiting the Sun. When they pass through the Earth's atmosphere, friction heats them, and they become incandescent.

Milky Way. The galaxy which includes the Sun and, hence, the Earth.

Moon. The natural satellite of the Earth. The Moon is such a (comparatively) large satellite that it is thought that Earth and Moon form a double planet system.

Nadir. The point vertically below the observer, where a vertical line through his position intersects the celestial sphere.

Nebula. A term embracing all kinds of nebulous objects in the sky, which could not be resolved into stars with earlier telescopes. Some are in fact galaxies outside the Milky Way, others are clusters of stars or clouds of matter within the Milky Way.

Neptune. Counting outwards from the Sun, Neptune is the eighth planet of the Solar System.

Node. The orbits of the planets are all in slightly different planes. The nodes are the two points where the orbit intersects the plane of the Earth's orbit, the *ecliptic.*

Nova. These are stars which suddenly become brighter. Their brightness reverts to its normal value after a few days or a few years. Novae are thought to be 'old' stars, expanding as they generate large amounts of energy.

Nutation. A small variation in the Earth's spinning on its axis.

Occultation. This happens when the Moon or one of the planets passes in front of another heavenly body.

Open Clusters. Groups of younger stars, together with loose gas and dust.

Opposition. The point in a planet's orbit when it is in the same line as the Sun and the Earth, with the Earth in the middle.

Orbit. The path taken by a heavenly body.

Parallax. An angle used in measuring the distance of stars. It is half the angle between the Earth at one end of its orbit, the star and the Earth at the other end of its orbit.

Parsec. A unit of distance, based on parallax. If the parallax angle is one second (1/3600 of a degree), then its distance is said to be one parsec.

1 parsec = 3.26 light years.

Penumbra. The less dark region of an eclipse shadow, surrounding the darker *umbra.*

Perigee. The point of the Moon's orbit where it is closest to the Earth.

Perihelion. The nearest point of a planet or comet to the Sun.

Phase. The different appearances of the Moon, Mercury or Venus, as a different portion of their illuminated hemisphere is seen from the Earth.

Photographic Magnitude. The magnitude of a star, as measured on a photographic plate. This is more sensitive to blue and ultraviolet light than is the eye. So, with stars of certain colours, it differs from the *visual magnitude.*

Photosphere. The visible surface of the Sun.

Pluto. The outermost planet of the Solar System.

Polaris. The star which marks, approximately, the position of the Earth's North Pole.

Populations. Divisions of stars according to their age. Older stars are called Population II and younger stars Population I.

Precession. Because the Earth is not quite spherical, its axis moves around, or *precesses.*

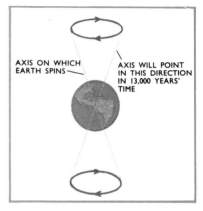

Prominence. A cloud of hot, luminous gas emitted from the Sun's surface.

Proper Motion. The movement of a star, relative to the Sun, causes its position to be slightly different each year. The difference in position each year is called the proper motion.

Radiation Pressure. The force exerted by any radiation (e.g. heat, light) on any object it strikes.

Radio Astronomy. A branch of Astronomy in which radio waves emitted by stars or clouds of matter are studied.

Radio Telescope. An instrument for collecting radio waves from stars or satellites.

Red Giant. A huge red star, e.g. Betelgeuse.

Red Shift. The 'shift' in the wavelength of light from a star towards the red end of the spectrum.

Revolution. The movement of a heavenly body in an orbit.

Right Ascension. A co-ordinate used in star maps.

Rills. Cracks on the Moon's surface, of unknown depth.

Rotation. The spinning movement of a heavenly body about its own axis.

Satellite. A heavenly body which revolves about a planet.

Saturn. The second largest planet of the Solar System, occupying the orbit beyond Jupiter.

Shooting Stars. Another name for meteors.

Sidereal Period. This is the time, as seen from the Sun, taken by a planet to complete one revolution around the Sun in relation to the stars.

Sidereal Time. Time based on the rotation of the celestial sphere.

Solar Constant. The total radiation received in one minute on a surface area of one square centimetre placed at right angles to the Sun's rays just outside the Earth's atmosphere.

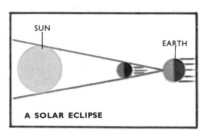

A SOLAR ECLIPSE

Solar Eclipse. The eclipse of the Sun. It occurs when the Moon comes directly between the Sun and the Earth.

Solar Energy. The energy emitted by the Sun, produced by thermonuclear reactions within the Sun.

Solar System. The Sun, together with its planets, their satellites, asteroids, meteorites, comets and dust.

Solstice (Summer and Winter). The positions on the *ecliptic* occupied by the Sun on the 21st or 22nd of June, and on the 21st or 22nd December.

Spectrohelioscope. An instrument used to photograph the Sun using light of one wavelength (i.e. monochromatic light).

Spectroscope. An instrument used to split up light received from a star into its constituent colours, which can then be examined individually

Spectroscopic Binaries. Two stars so close together that they appear, when viewed through a telescope, as one. Their double nature can be observed only when their light is split up in a spectroscope.

Spicules. Moving wisps of matter in the Sun's chromosphere.

Spiral Galaxy. Galaxies, like the Milky Way, where the brightest stars are concentrated in the spiral arms of a disc.

Star. A large, hot gaseous body, like the Sun, which emits its own light.

Star Cluster. A group of stars which are actually clustered together (and do not just appear to be so, as seen from the Earth).

Sun. The star nearest the Earth, and the source of practically all its energy.

Sunspot. A darker patch on the Sun's photosphere, two thousand degrees cooler than the rest of the Sun.

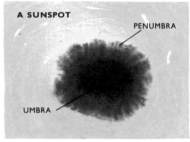

A SUNSPOT

PENUMBRA

UMBRA

Supergiant. An extra-large star.

Superior Planets. Planets whose orbits lie outside the Earth's.

Surge. A short-lived disturbance in the Sun's chromosphere.

Synodic Period. The time a member of the Solar System takes to complete one revolution, as seen from the Earth.

Tides. The high and low water levels on the Earth are caused mainly by the gravitational pull of the Moon, and to a lesser extent by the Sun. Tides also occur on binary stars, because of the gravitational pull of each star on the other's surface.

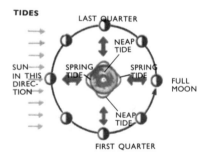

TIDES

LAST QUARTER
NEAP TIDE
SUN IN THIS DIRECTION
SPRING TIDE
SPRING TIDE
FULL MOON
NEAP TIDE
FIRST QUARTER

Transit. A transit occurs when one of the members of the Solar System moves across the disc of another member (e.g. when Mercury or Venus, as seen from the Earth, moves across the Sun's disc).

Triangulation. This is a method of measuring the distances of the nearer stars. The required distance forms one of the sides of a triangle, and the radius of the Earth's orbit another. The distance is found indirectly by measuring the angles of the triangle.

Twinkling of Stars. Stars do not, themselves, twinkle. The effect is produced by small changes in the refractive index of the Earth's atmosphere.

Umbra. The darkest areas of the shadow cast during an eclipse, or the darkest, central part of a sunspot.

Universe. All space, and everything within it.

Uranus. The third largest planet of the Solar System. Because it is so far from the Earth (it occupies the orbit beyond Saturn) it was not discovered until the 18th century.

Van Allen Belts. These are belts of charged particles surrounding the Earth. They were discovered with the aid of artificial satellites.

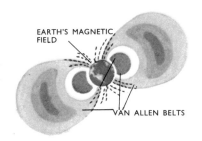

Variable Stars. Stars whose brightness varies. The brightness of some stars varies regularly. Three per cent of all visible stars are variable stars.

Velocity of Escape. This is the velocity a body needs to have before it can escape from the gravitational pull of a heavenly body.

Venus. The planet which comes the closest to the Earth. However, very little is known about it, because it is always covered by dense clouds.

Vernal Equinox. The point where the Sun apparently passes from the Southern Hemisphere to the Northern Hemisphere of the celestial sphere.

Visual Binary. A pair of stars close together, but distinguishable from each other with a telescope.

Visual Magnitude. The magnitude of a star, as seen by the eye. It may differ from the *photographic magnitude*.

Walled Plains. Large 'craters' on the Moon.

Year. There are several different measurements of this. The *anomalistic year* is the time taken to orbit the Sun once, from perihelion to perihelion. A *sidereal year* is the time taken by the Sun to return to a fixed position among the stars. The *tropical year* is the time between two transits (by the Sun) of the vernal equinox.

Zenith. The point on the celestial sphere immediately above the observer.

Zodiac. The part of the celestial sphere around the Sun's apparent path on the sphere. There are 12 important constellations in it.

Zodiacal Light. A faint cone of light visible after sunset and before sunrise. It is thought to be sunlight reflected by dust in the space between the Sun and the Earth.

Index